APPROACHING
FREE
ENERGY

by the Editors of Rodale's NEW SHELTER®

CONTENTS

Note on Prices:

Due to the effects of inflation and the fluctuation of the dollar against foreign currencies, the reader should assume that the prices quoted in the following articles are generally low. Please use the quoted prices as guides and referents, not as fact.

APPROACHING FREE ENERGY

These Three Homes Show the Way

In Longmont, Colorado, the neighbors worry about rising fuel costs and blustery Rocky Mountain winters. But the Eckenrodes are concerned only that the warranty on their furnace will run out before the unit is ever actually used to heat their home.

Much further north, in a suburban home outside Regina, Saskatchewan, Bob and Carol Tangeman confidently expect to pay under $50 to heat their two-story 2,000-square-foot home during the long Canadian winter.

Near Princeton, New Jersey, the Horton family lives in a row home that outwardly is identical to the others in its block, yet consumes only one-third the heating fuel used by its next-door neighbors.

These three homes exemplify a new era of practical, efficient dwellings that can be heated and cooled inexpensively (or for free) without exotic solar collectors, bizarre floor plans or huge investments. The first two are new homes that employ a variety of low-cost energy conservation methods. Both virtually heat themselves, but their construction costs were just seven percent higher than the same floor plans without the efficiency-boosting additions. The Princeton row home is a standardly built structure that has been retrofitted with just $425 worth of materials to slash its fuel use by an incredible 66 percent.

These homes are not "magic shows" of arcane technology. In fact, the most unusual aspect of these homes is that there is *nothing* unusual about their techniques. A list of these techniques sounds almost banal: Insulation, weather stripping, waste heat recovery, and (in the case of new construction) proper siting, orientation, and so on.

The Eckenrodes, Tangemans, and Hortons are quietly proving that right now, inexpensive conservation techniques can cut a new home's fuel bill to practically nothing for the life of the dwelling, and existing homes can use two-thirds less fuel each and every year.

Little Things Add Up

It might seem obvious to say, "every home is different," but that statement is revolutionizing the way we look at houses. For years, designers and builders regarded homes as idealized boxes

5

of warm air sitting in a cold environment. (Or, in the case of southern climates, as boxes of cool air in a hot environment.) In such a simple setting, it's easy to juggle R-factors, insulation thicknesses, vapor barriers and other design elements to arrive at an estimate of any home's energy needs. Unfortunately, these figures had little bearing on real homes built in the real world. Instead of a theoretically neat layer of insulation, real homes have damaged or missing batts, or insulation whose properties are diminished by condensed water. Instead of a continuous vapor stop, real houses have barriers pierced by pipes, cables and by accidental gaps and rips. Instead of an enclosed, stable environment, real dwellings must contend with capricious winds, and with occupants who open and close windows and doors as part of their routine of living.

These variances from textbook ideals add up to significant differences from one home to the next. In fact, a recent study examined pairs of seemingly identical townhouses located only a few dozen feet apart, and built by the same crew at the same time with the same materials. On paper, they were completely identical, yet researchers found that energy use in some houses was *twice* that of others.

The reason for this difference was traced to apparently picayune flaws in sealing and insulation: although each defect was tiny in itself, as a whole they added up to a doubling of fuel bills. Findings like these mean that the new first law of energy conservation is to prevent these flaws from occurring in new homes, and to detect and eliminate these flaws in existing dwellings.

New Priorities

The table on page 13 graphically illustrates these new findings. Most of us think ceilings are the primary route by which a home loses its heat, but as you can see, infiltration turns out to be the largest single energy drain, followed by basement or foundation losses, door and window losses, wall losses, and *last*, ceiling losses. This means that blowing extra insulation into your attic may actually be the least effective means of reducing your home's fuel use, while attacking infiltration losses is the most effective. It's a matter of getting the priorities straight.

In new homes and old, infiltration losses easily can be cut in half by a careful, painstaking tracing of all the many avenues by which cool air can enter the home and warm air can leave. Once infiltration has been dealt with, there are dozens of other steps that can be taken to make a home come ever closer to the idea of zero-energy use.

In new homes, for instance, you can orient the floor plan on an east-west line so that one of the home's long walls faces south. Place at least 80 percent of the home's windows on the sunny south side, and equip them with thermal shutters, drapes or curtains. Provide awnings or overhangs to protect the windows from overheating in summer. In cool climates, choose a dark color for the roof and walls to maximize heat absorption. In warm areas, light shades such as white or yellow help reject excess solar energy.

In existing homes, make sure your heating system is in top shape, and that all heating pipes and ducts are insulated. Add thermal shutters to windows, or use insulating drapes or curtains to help hold in the heat. Choose appliances for efficiency with an eye to their contribution to the home's total energy loads.

Why bother? Because tightening up any home, whether it's a design just in the planning stages, or a 150-year-old farmhouse, provides greater financial benefits in less time than any other home energy strategy. Tightening up in a thorough, craftsmanlike manner means quick returns on your investment, and payback times sometimes measured in months or even weeks, instead of decades.

Let's go back to those three outstanding homes mentioned earlier to see how they embody various conservation methods, and to discover what it's like to live in a super-efficient home.

Longmont, Colorado

About two years ago, Chuck and Jane Eckenrode were living in what Jane describes as "a nice little house in suburbia," with plenty of bedrooms, a family room . . . and high heating bills.

Chuck was interested in solar collectors but was put off by price tags and long payback times. Then Jane ran across an ad in the local Sunday paper for an 1,800-square-foot home with an attached two-car garage. The house was being designed and built by Paul Shippee of Colorado Sun Works, and was to include the latest in conservation technologies. It was to be made of poured reinforced concrete, completely enveloped in a thick layer of polystyrene insulation and provided with a 3,000-gallon drumwall heat-storage system. Bermed on top and on the east, west and north sides, the only exposed wall would face due south and be extensively glazed. The glazing would be protected by a Beadwall movable insulation system, and by a carefully designed roof overhang. Sunscoop skylights would provide natural illumination throughout the home. Along with all that, the house was to feature a livable, attractive floor plan.

At first the Eckenrodes didn't know what all the details meant, but went to watch the construction in progress, to scrutinize carefully the design specifications, and to learn the new terminology. They liked what they saw, and in October of 1977, they moved in.

"It's a good design," Chuck told me. "It looks exotic, but it's really nothing more than common sense. Now that we've lived in the house for a while, and we know that it works, we want others to know that there are better alternatives to conventional housing."

Jane agrees. "A lot of people ask what we would change if we had to do it over again. Chuck and I have talked this over, and we have a one-word answer: 'Nothing.'"

Visiting the house, which is bright, spacious, and filled with tropical plants, it's easy to see why the Eckenrodes feel so strongly. Their home is testament to the fact that beauty and efficiency can coexist, and even complement one another.

The key to this home's efficiency lies in a variety of conservation measures. The poured concrete is insulated on the *outside* so that the masonry remains at room temperature; protected from cold outside temperatures by a thick layer of waterproof polystyrene insulation. The drumwall heat-storage system consists of fifty-three 55-gallon drums which are painted flat black and stacked alongside the south-facing windows. Containing a total of almost 3,000 gallons of water, these drums absorb en-

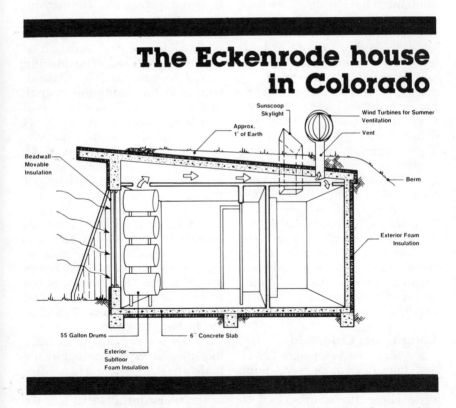

The Eckenrode house in Colorado

The south side of the Eckenrode's home shows the drumwall behind the floor-to-ceiling double glazing, the overhang which protects the windows from the hot summer sun, and the two slanted enclosures which house the solar water heaters.

ergy from the sunlight shining through the windows, and give it back to the living areas at night by natural convection and radiation. Together, the drumwall and the insulated masonry provide a huge thermal mass to temper the home's internal climate. In order for the air inside the house to cool off one degree, thousands of pounds of concrete and water also have to cool off, which delays the process many hours.

Where Your Home Loses Heat

Most people believe that ceilings are the principal path of heat loss in their homes. Although this was once true, modern standards of construction have changed the equation of heat loss and gain so that infiltration now heads the list.

ceiling 15%
walls 15%
basement 25%
doors and windows 15%
infiltration 30%

The berms, or earthen embankments, shelter the north, east and west walls of the house from cold temperatures and the bitter prairie winds, creating a warm, draft-free interior environment. The roof receives similar protection from a full foot of soil graded into a graceful little hill. In addition to providing climate tempering, the berms also limit maintenance of most of the home's exterior to an occasional mowing of the natural grasses that cover the berming.

The Beadwall movable insulation system consists of a wall glazed with parallel panes of plate glass spaced five inches apart. In sunny weather, the wall looks and operates like any standard floor-to-ceiling double-glazed window, letting in reams of light and free heat. But at night or in cloudy weather, blowers force millions of tiny polystyrene beads between the panes of glass, filling the space, and turning the windows into an opaque white wall with better insulating qualities than standard wooden frame walls. Operation of the Beadwalls is automatic, with manual overrides for flexibility—and fun.

"I guess they are a bit of a toy for me," Chuck admitted, as we watched the windows fill and empty like huge rectangular hourglasses.

"They really are," said Jane. "The first few weeks we were here, those beads went up and down more times. . . ."

The sunscoop skylights are triple-glazed, periscopelike devices that extend from the ceiling up through the berms. Painted a reflective white on the insides, the sunscoops catch the low winter sunlight and provide ample natural illumination throughout the home's light-colored interior, even on gray days. In summer, when the sun is high in the sky, the skylight's carefully designed interior angles prevent direct sunlight from shining into the home, minimizing warm-weather overheating.

It's no puzzle why Chuck and Jane Eckenrode are smiling. It's below freezing outside, there's snow on the ground, but their house is heated and illuminated solely by the sun.

Finally, two solar-powered water preheaters are mounted in slanted enclosures on the home's exposed south wall, and collect enough sunlight, in both summer and winter, to keep the Eckenrode's gas water heating bills at a paltry $7 per month.

In all, the sun provides fully 75 percent of the home's total heating needs, with the balance coming from lights, appliances and the inhabitants.

The house is so well built that there have been few start-up problems, and maintenance is

From the cold north side, little can be seen of the Eckenrode's home. Visible here are five sunscoops, the fireplace chimney, the railing of the rooftop deck, and the few northside windows which local building codes require for bedroom fire exits.

Sunscoop skylights reduce the need for artificial lighting and help minimize electric bills. This photo was taken entirely with the light given off by one sunscoop.

minimal. In fact, the most serious problem facing the Eckenrodes is how to contend with curious passersby.

"Before the berm was contoured and planted," Chuck said, "people would drive up and ask, 'What is this? A potato cellar? A store?' There was even one time I was changing my clothes in the bedroom, and I looked up and saw a 70-year-old woman with her face pressed up against the Beadwall, looking in."

"At first, we took some kidding from our friends," Jane

continued, "because our house is different on the outside from theirs. But then we'd sit down and compare heating bills. We're the ones laughing now."

The operating costs *are* very low. In addition to the solar water heaters, the sunscoops minimize the need for artificial lighting, so electric use (which includes the lighting, refrigerator and kitchen range) averages just $25 per month. In all, the Eckenrodes estimate that they save $500 a heating season over what they'd have to pay for energy in a conventionally built home of the same size. And because the house stays cool in summer, there's no need for air conditioning so, the cooling season savings are substantial as well.

Efficiency is important, but it's not everything. Just as significant, the Eckenrode's home is designed for comfort. Normal day-to-night temperature fluctuations average just four degrees and, under harsh conditions, the house stays comfortably warm for up to three sunless days. In that time, interior temperatures might drop around ten degrees. On rare occasions when there's no sun for four or more days, Chuck builds a small fire in a heatilator-type fireplace which uses outside air for combustion, so none of the home's heat goes up the chimney. The Eckenrodes have switched on their gas back-up heating system only twice: once just to see if it worked, and once so their five-year-old daughter, who had just broken a leg, could sleep com-

fortably without blankets. Other than that, the sun has done virtually all the work of keeping their home comfortably warm and brightly lit.

The house also has a quality that only can be described as peaceful: with passive solar heating, there are no pumps or blowers. The berms filter out almost all exterior noises, and eliminate all drafts. Gazing out across miles of frozen Colorado prairie from the quiet and comfort of a bright, warm living room, heated and lighted by the sun, is an experience guaranteed to win over even the most hardened fossil-fuel junkie.

"I like to live comfortably," said Jane, "and this is the way to do it."

Chuck smiled and stretched out on the rug, which was warm from the solar heat stored in the insulated concrete floor beneath it. "We could have bought a bigger house," he said, "or a different one. But I don't think we could have bought a better one."

Regina, Saskatchewan

When I arrived at the Tangeman's house in early November, it was 8° F and snowing. "Welcome to Saskatchewan," Bob said. "We have just two seasons here: July and winter. You missed July."

"But this isn't *cold*," said Carol. "Our first house was next to a railroad, and the first winter we were here, I heard this high, soft metallic noise, sort of a *zinnnng*. It was so cold, the rail-

Filling the Beadwalls is a visually spectacular operation which converts the floor-to-ceiling windows to opaque white walls. Once the polystyrene beads are in place, the windows are better insulated than most standard wooden frame walls.

The Beadwalls (seen here from the plant-filled living room atrium) take about six minutes to fill or empty. Operation is automatic, with manual overrides.

The Tangeman's home in Saskatchewan is one of the most thermally efficient in the world, with an exterior designed to blend well into its suburban environs.

13

road tracks were singing. Now, *that's* cold."

We retreated to their living room, which was cheerful and warm despite the miserable weather outside.

The Tangemans live in the "Saskatchewan Conservation House," a structure built by the Canadian government to demonstrate that conservation techniques can work even in a severely cold climate.

From the outside, the house looks fairly conventional, and fits in with its suburban neighborhood. Unlike the Eckenrode's Colorado home, there isn't much to see from the street that would

The Tangeman family relaxes in the short-sleeve comfort of the Conservation House, despite the bitter temperatures outside.

Thick R-22 shutters fold down over the home's largest windows at night. They're electrically operated from switches mounted in the living room.

The smaller windows in the house are equipped with interior sliding shutters which are closed at sunset and opened at breakfast.

lead you to believe the Tangeman's house is one of the most thermally efficient in the world.

Most Canadian homes built in the 1970s have roofs insulated to R-12. The Conservation House is superinsulated, with foot-thick walls filled with fiberglass and cellulose to R-40, a heavy layer of R-60 cellulose insulation in the ceiling, and a crawlspace protected from frigid weather with R-40 polystyrene and fiberglass. Built as a no-nonsense cube,

which exposes a minimum amount of exterior wall per square foot of floor space, it's painted brown to absorb as much solar radiation as possible.

Inside, the house is virtually airtight and draft-free. A vapor barrier three times thicker than standard plastic sheeting was installed without gaps or rips, and was carefully sealed with a puttylike material at every seam. Each electrical outlet was isolated in its own airtight plastic

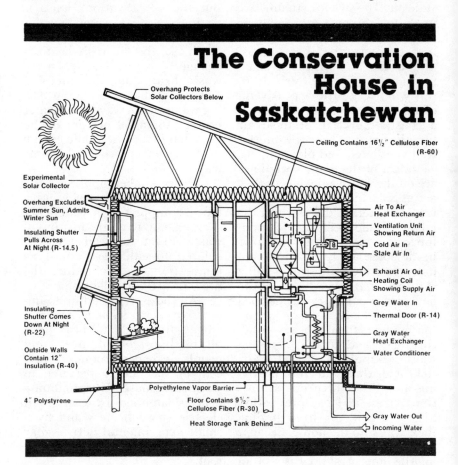

The Conservation House in Saskatchewan

Overhang Protects Solar Collectors Below

Ceiling Contains 16½″ Cellulose Fiber (R-60)

Experimental Solar Collector

Overhang Excludes Summer Sun, Admits Winter Sun

Insulating Shutter Pulls Across At Night (R-14.5)

Air To Air Heat Exchanger

Ventilation Unit Showing Return Air

Cold Air In
Stale Air In

Exhaust Air Out
Heating Coil Showing Supply Air

Grey Water In

Insulating Shutter Comes Down At Night (R-22)

Thermal Door (R-14)

Gray Water Heat Exchanger

Water Conditioner

Outside Walls Contain 12″ Insulation (R-40)

4″ Polystyrene

Polyethylene Vapor Barrier

Floor Contains 9½″ Cellulose Fiber (R-30)

Heat Storage Tank Behind

Gray Water Out
Incoming Water

enclosure, and every pipe or cable passing through a wall or floor was caulked until airtight.

These steps made the Conservation House so well-sealed that a special heat exchanger had to be installed on the second floor to keep the home's air from becoming stale and unhealthful. The heat exchanger uses two low-wattage fans to pull a small amount of fresh air into the home, while simultaneously exhausting the same amount of stale air. The two air streams are made to flow past each other in opposite directions within the heat exchanger, so that almost all the stale air's heat is given up to the incoming cold, fresh air. In this way, very little heat is vented to the outside, and yet there is a constant cycling of fresh air into the home to keep the interior well ventilated and pleasant.

Most of the home's windows are on the south side, where they act as solar collectors. Thick exterior shutters fold down over the largest windows at night to minimize heat losses. Other windows in the house are fitted with manually operated interior sliding shutters that also hold in the heat. The front entry is equipped with three doors: a storm door on the outside, then a heavy solid-core door and finally, across a short vestibule, a virtually airtight door that leads into the living area. The three doors function as an airlock, preventing blasts of cold air from finding their way into the home. Because the house is so well sealed, closing the innermost door is a bit of a surprise. As the door swings shut for the last few inches of travel, you can actually feel air resistance try to keep the door open. It's a little like trying to close the door on a Volkswagen *Bug*.

But conservation doesn't end with airtight construction and heavy insulation. In standard homes, a significant amount of energy literally goes down the drain as hot dirty water from washing, cooking and bathing. But the Conservation House is equipped with a water-to-water heat exchanger which operates much like the air-to-air heat exchanger described earlier, using waste heat from the outgoing water to preheat the cold incoming water on its way to the water heater. About 50 percent of the heat that otherwise would end up in the sewer is recovered in this way.

Every kitchen appliance has been selected for efficiency, every tap is equipped with water-conserving devices to minimize waste. All interior walls are light colored to enhance natural illumination, and to reduce the need for artificial lighting.

All these steps add up to impressive energy savings. The sun, along with incidental heat given off by lights, appliances, and people, provides around 75 percent of the energy required to warm the house. The remaining heat is supplied by two small electric space heaters and by a small experimental active solar collection system installed on the roof.

On the outside, the Horton's home looks much like others in the neighborhood. Yet inside, a series of inexpensive conservation measures are racking up huge energy savings, each and every month.

Even low-level heat, such as that produced while baking this casserole, helps the Hortons stay warm all night with minimal help from the furnace.

Bifold shutters, each covering half the window area on the home's south side, are drawn at night to conserve heat. Drapes mounted directly on the shutters allow for conventional decorative touches.

So little additional heat is needed that the Tangemans use a microwave oven for cooking. "If I used a conventional oven," said Carol, "we'd drive ourselves out of the house with overheating." In fact, almost any heat source, however small, raises the home's temperature and helps the Tangemans live comfortably without a furnace. "Oh, it feels just great when the sun shines in. You notice it right away," Carol said.

Bob agreed. "The house is so tight, so well insulated, that we can shut everything down at bedtime, go all night without any heat input, and it'll only be about four degrees cooler when we get up in the morning. Really, this house is one of the nicest, easiest and least unsavory ways to save energy I know of. It fits right in with our life-style. After the first week or so, for example, the kids stopped talking about the shutters and doors. I think they'd be talking a lot more if they had to split wood or shovel coal. Living here is painlessly efficient."

"And the house takes care of itself," added Carol. "Anyone could move into a house like this and have minimal adjustments. Just five minutes a day to open and close the shutters and you're done."

When it was time to leave, Bob walked me to the door. "The important thing to remember is that there's nothing really exotic about this house," he concluded. "It's mostly off-the-shelf components. I think you could take just about any house, insulate it well, like this one, maybe use a little more south-side glass with shutters or some other closure, and your heating costs would go right down to zero. The only secret is to use great care."

That *is* the secret. There was no magic to these houses, or to their minuscule energy bills. All that was needed was great care in their design and construction. And that same great care can be applied just as effectively to existing houses, as a row home in New Jersey clearly demonstrates.

Twin Rivers, New Jersey

"Nitty gritty little things that don't sound spectacular are the first step in successful energy conservation. The trick is to be clever and cheap."

Frank Sinden, a senior research scientist who divides his time between Princeton University and Bell Laboratories, was talking about his experience with the Twin Rivers retrofit project, one of the nation's most comprehensive studies of how existing dwellings could be made more efficient.

"Really, to begin, all you need are your eyes and your hands. Just looking around a house and feeling with your fingers will tell you where the major leaks are. You have to snoop around; to get right into the attic, for example, and pull up some insulation to look for unsealed openings in the ceiling. Sometimes batts are missing or damaged. Sometimes there is no vapor barrier, or a poor one, so warm air from the house flows right past the insulation as though it isn't there."

Frank was speaking both from his considerable theoretical knowledge as a scientist and from his direct experience with retrofits. In the early '70s, a new suburban housing development was chosen as a study target to see where domestic energy was being wasted and what could be done about it. Townhouses and row homes in the Twin Rivers development were selected as typical of contemporary construction standards and materials. Teams of technicians and scientists—Frank Sinden among

them—moved in with truckloads of monitoring equipment and new ideas. While other teams fanned out to measure energy consumption in a variety of homes, Frank and his co-workers selected one house, more or less at random, and decided to do everything they could to make it more efficient without altering the basic structure or relying on high-tech fixes. It was through this firsthand experience that Frank learned where to look for heat leaks.

"You've got to check around every pipe, every duct, and every place a wire or cable runs through a partition. Each house is different, so you have to look carefully. You could look around a clothes dryer vent in one home and find nothing, while in another, you'd see daylight through the crack. Not one of these heat leaks is critical in itself, but together they add up to quite a lot. And it's important to be hard-nosed about the economics, because million-dollar fixes just aren't going to be used widely. When we decided to build insulating shutters, for example, I built them myself in my basement from chipboard, Masonite and glass wool, trying to be as cheap as I could be, not to be cute, but to make sure that our fixes could be afforded and used by almost everyone."

Frank's approach worked. With only $425 worth of materials, the Princeton group cut infiltration in the test home by more than half, which led to a reduction in fuel use by a full 66

Interior storm doors protect the north side of the Horton's New Jersey home from heat loss escaping through the large patio doors.

percent. The homemade shutters were the most sophisticated device used, with the rest of the retrofit being limited to caulking, weather stripping and extra insulation.

"All these things are very ordinary and mundane," Frank said, "but the enormous savings we achieved point out that these are exactly the sort of things that need to be done in most homes. This type of conservation should be right at the top of everyone's list. Eliminating an electric toothbrush is a lousy way to save electricity if there's an uninsulated water tank in the basement. I don't know why, but it's hard to get people to realize this."

Bob and Nina Horton, who purchased the retrofitted home after the Princeton group had finished its test, agree wholeheartedly. "It's frustrating trying to get people to do in their homes what we have done here," said Bob. "I talk about making houses airtight, and people say 'Oh, I added extra insulation in my attic, too.' What they don't realize is that you've got to do more than just lay in a few extra batts of insulation. You've got to pay attention to a host of seemingly insignificant details which, in sum, add up to enormous savings."

Bob shook his head sadly, "You know, I wish Frank had installed a mysterious black box here in my living room, one equipped with lots of flashing lights and twitching meters. That way, I'd have an eye-catching gadget to point to and say, 'This is what's trimming 60 percent off my fuel bills.' I think people would stampede out to buy a black box of their own. Instead, I take visitors down to my basement to show how carefully my foundation's been sealed, and they say 'Ho hum,' even though small retrofits like that could save them hundreds of dollars."

$100 = $3650

"Low Cost, No Cost," a pamphlet published by the Department of Energy, shows how an investment of about $100 and a few hours time can cut your heating bills by as much as 25 percent.

Using these figures, and assuming an annual energy budget of $500, a homeowner's first year conservation savings would be $125. Because the materials cost $100, the first year profits are $25. After that, the savings accrue at the full $125 rate annually, which amounts to $3,650 over the life of an average mortgage. If rising fuel costs and inflation are figured in, the savings are even more impressive.

The energy-saving tips offered in the pamphlet can be implemented in a spare weekend or two, and require few tools more complex than scissors and screwdrivers. In all, these ideas add up to tremendous savings in energy and money with minimal cost and effort.

To obtain a copy of "Low Cost, No Cost," write to the DOE's Technical Information Center, Box 62, Oak Ridge, TN 37830.

Most of the spectacular energy savings in the Horton's home come from seemingly minor retrofits like these sealed joints between the wooden framing and masonry foundation.

Despite these frustrations, the Hortons find that living efficiently blends in with their comfortable suburban life. "We're happy with the move," says Nina. "We really didn't have to make any adjustments to live here. Oh, I have to spend two minutes a day to open or close the shutters, but I used to pull the drapes on our old house anyway, and that took just as long. Living here is very ordinary, very comfortable, and yet we're saving tremendous amounts of energy and money. We're very satisfied."

They have every reason to be. The original investment of $425 in materials has already repaid itself many times over. The fuel bills average $15 a month, and never top $35 a month, even in the worst winter weather. These savings are even more remarkable when you remember that this is a conventional house, built with materials and techniques used nationwide. It's probably a home like yours.

Frank Sinden summed it up very well: "It's like shooting fish in a bucket to save 20 or 30 or even 40 percent on average fuel bills. There's a tremendous, *staggering* potential for savings that's just waiting to be tapped. It gets a little tougher to save the next 30 percent, but still it can be done, and without too much difficulty."

THE SUNSPACE

A nice way to prepare for the 1980s

How can you get the sun to heat your nonsolar home? There are only a handful of ways. Some work better than others, depending on the house and climate. They vary in price and difficulty of construction. And if you've never seen one before, they can look strange.

Except the sunspace.

What is a sunspace? It's so new it doesn't have a standard name. It has been called a sun room, a solar room, an attached solar greenhouse, even a walk-in solar collector.

What does a sunspace do? It captures enough sunlight to heat itself and part of your house. It provides a welcome environment for growing plants. And if you work things right, it can be used for producing food all year-round, even in the farthest reaches of the snowbelt.

How can it do that? The scientific principle is called the "greenhouse effect," and it's what makes solar heating possible. You already have a seat-of-the-pants lesson in this when you get into a closed car on a hot day. The inside of the car heats up because the windows permit more energy to enter the car than can return back out. In this way, the sun's radiant energy becomes trapped heat. The earth's atmosphere works in the same way as a car's windshield. It allows the earth to accumulate heat by trapping radiant energy.

But the enterprise of sun-collecting doesn't stop there. If it did, mammoth commercial greenhouses would be efficient solar energy collectors instead of notorious wasters of fossil fuel. One reason an ordinary greenhouse isn't "solar" is because it doesn't *store* the heat that enters it. Solar structures store heat by incorporating *thermal mass*, generally water or masonry.

Thermal mass is used to make structures cooler by day and warmer by night. The sunspaces in the Ozarks and Oregon

Attached sunspace with interior shutters and reversible heat reflecting/absorbing panel. Home of Roberta and Holman Davis, Brunswick, Maine.

we've featured in the following pages use 55-gallon drums of water. You don't normally think of water acting like a sponge, but in the realm of solar energy that's how it works. It "soaks up" the sun's heat during the day, but gives back all that heat to the sunspace at night because it takes almost all night to cool off. Another way of explaining it is this: boil 10 gallons of water in one pot and put 10 teaspoonfuls in another. Shut both off when they reach a boil. The one which takes longer to boil and cool down completely is the more massive amount, of course. That's the principle behind "thermal mass."

You can store heat because heat is a form of energy, and energy can be changed only into other forms of energy. It cannot be destroyed. But it *will* slip through your fingers if you aren't careful. Because heat invariably dissipates to places cooler than itself, you have to seal it in to keep it. That means carefully insulating the side walls of your sunspaces, weather-stripping all entries, providing two layers of glazing and, ideally, some form of insulation that covers the glazing at night.

You don't have to store heat in your sunspace. You can draw it into your house, then tightly seal off the openings to the sunspace at night and let it get cold in there. The mass of your house; its walls, floors and so forth, will then store some heat for a little while into the evening.

Ah, but during the day . . . that's why the sunspace is so nice. Of all the ways to solarize an existing home, the sunspace is the only one that's more than a gizmo. It's kind to plants, and kind to people. It's a place to live. It's a solar home in miniature.

If sunspaces are so great, why didn't anyone think of them sooner? In a way, they did. The ancient Roman aristocrats used large expanses of glass to make a sun room in their houses. In England in the mid-1800s, a favorite architectural touch on upper class homes was the glass-enclosed conservatory. More than merely an attached greenhouse, the conservatory was a popular winter gathering spot in which to read, talk, play cards and be cheered by lovely sunlight. And in Scandinavia between the two world wars, architects experimented with the heat value of south-facing glass-bedecked rooms.

Here in America, it took the 1973 oil embargo and the end of cheap energy to get us rolling. Within the last five years the sunspace has become a solar solution that has been developed and championed by innovators from many quarters. It has seemingly popped out of nowhere, yet it has been adapted in a remarkably brief time to urban tenements, suburban palaces and rural chicken houses alike. It is, we think, the best way to bring the sun into your nonsolar home.

All it asks is a south wall and a caring owner.

Mark wanted headroom in his 45-degree-angled greenhouse, so he dug the floor nearly four feet below ground. Side vents open in the summer to allow excess heat to escape.

Mark Davis's greenhouse cost him $733.00. In return, it helped reduce his heating fuel requirements by one-third and provided him with year-round vegetables.

In Oregon:
Heat and Greens

Mark Davis's sunspace works so well, he has used only slightly more than one cord of wood last winter to heat his western Oregon home. That compares with three cords of wood he burned the previous winter.

True, some of that savings had to be attributed to the insulation he put in the west wall of his 30-year-old house. The increased tightness, plus a smallish space heating load to begin with (Mark's house is 1,000 square feet) allowed his solar addition to really do its stuff.

To Mark, a vegetarian, the free heat gain is like pennies from Heaven. What he chiefly requires of his sunspace is food during the months his garden is out of commission. That means the temperature in his plant-growing area must not dip below 40° F. To insure that, Mark has placed a dozen water-filled 55-gallon drums against the back wall of his sunspace.

Mark's 12 barrels evidently provide enough thermal mass to do the trick. The coldest his sunspace got last winter was 41° F one night. And that was after a ten-day stretch of sunless, subfreezing weather.

To get so much heat *and* food from an 8x16-foot sunspace with 181 square feet of glazing in the cloudy Northwest ought to give Mark a great sense of accomplishment. It did. Here are more details of how he did it.

The floor of Mark's sunspace is 42 inches below the earth's surface. According to Mark, the main reason for "digging in" was headroom. "I just wanted to use a simple 45-degree angle on the glazed portion of the greenhouse. My latitude is 45 degrees and that number plus 15 would be considered the 'optimum' angle by most solar engineers but just a simple 45 degree is easier to build. I also wanted to start that angle just under the roof eaves, which are eight feet high. So, if I wanted to be able to stand up in the thing anywhere except right along the house wall I was forced to sink the floor into the earth."

The tactic yielded an unexpected result. The interior height "allows the hot air in the sunspace to flow into the living space of the house without the use of fans or other expensive hardware," Mark says. Warm air enters the house through two double-hung windows already there before the sunspace.

The construction of the below-grade portion was done with a poured concrete footing on which concrete block walls were laid. The outsides of the walls were lined with rigid insulating boards. Then a concrete floor was poured in place.

Mark framed the superstructure with 2 x 4s and nailed flat Filon glazing to the outer edge of the studs. For a second layer of glazing Mark tacked a sheet of clear polyethylene plastic to the inside of the framework. He closed in both the east and west walls of the sunspace with plywood sheeting on the interior and exterior, and placed 3½-inch

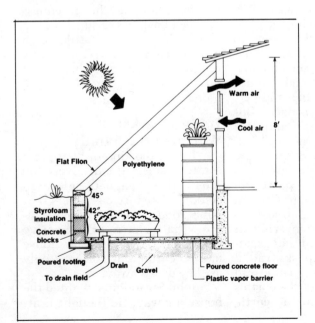

fiberglass batts in the spaces between the studs. On both the east and west walls he built 16 x 16-inch vents close to the apex of the sunspace. The vents are operated manually to allow summer heat to escape. The 12 water-filled drums are then stacked against the north wall where direct sunlight can strike them most of the day.

Mark started construction of his sunspace, with the help of his brother, in August 1978 and finished filling the last drum with water on Christmas Day. "There were a lot of other things I was doing at the same time," he says, "such as residing and painting the front of the house. If I considered just the time I spent building the sunspace itself, that would amount to about two weeks."

Mark's records show the total construction cost was $733.

Night insulation for the glazing is a feature Mark intends to add soon. "I'm sure that a movable insulating blanket or panel to cover the Filon at night would increase the overall thermal performance of the sunspace. But I'm directing my money and time right now to improving the insulation in my home. Besides, the sunspace is doing very well without the night covering, partly because of our western Oregon weather pattern. We almost always have a cloud covering at night around here and that greatly reduces the 'deep sky radiation' phenomenon." (A cloud cover reflects some of the earth's radiant heat back to the earth, but there is no such "blanket" for the earth on a clear night. That's why clear nights are colder.)

As frosting on the cake, the sunspace saved Mark money on his Oregon income tax. The state allows 25 percent of the cost of a sunspace (or other solar energy device) as a tax credit. That means Mark saved $183.25 on his taxes. So his sunspace really cost only $549.75. Nice state, Oregon.

But money doesn't tell the whole story. "If you wanted to put a strict dollar-and-cents return on the bucks I invested in my sunspace, it wouldn't be difficult to figure a value for the wood it saved me and how many dollars' worth of vegetables and greens it provided. But there is something else there. . . . When you go into the greenhouse in winter, when it is cold and snowy outside, and you can sit down, lay back among the greenness and just bask in the sunshine . . . just soak it in . . . it supplies a bone-warming power. It really revitalizes you. You just can't buy something like that with money."

In the Ozarks:
Warming the Family

It was the kind of house real estate agents dread. Even the most silver-tongued salesman couldn't convince customers that dank rooms and peephole windows had charm. Prospective customers admitted the house had potential, but voiced it only as they drove away.

John Strandquist wanted the house anyway. He thought it attractive, especially considering its low price. In Berryville, Arkansas, that was no small matter, since land was nearly as scarce as money. Besides, he was desperate: the family could no longer live in the hills in a shack without running water. Colleen, three months pregnant, simply couldn't haul buckets from the backyard pump anymore.

His relatives told him to wait. "Whatever you do," his mother-in-law advised, "don't tell Colleen about it until you're sure. She'll have you moved in

The kneewall is dropped down during the day to permit sunlight to bounce off the reflective surface, pass through the interior glass and be retained as heat by water-filled drums.

two weeks." John proved her wrong. His wife moved in one.

In the autumn of 1977, the house began to take shape. Colleen and John set up bunk beds for the boys, coaxed the wood stove to life and varnished the furniture. With a little paint and a lot of love, the house became a home.

By winter, however, their enthusiasm had vanished. The house was no longer just a challenge; it was a burden. The timid Arkansas winter became a tyrant and for the first time, the family spent nearly $50 a month on fuel. John's place of business, a local stone quarry, closed till spring. The baby was coming, and Colleen's feet hurt. Those winter nights, John would peer from the living room cubbyholes, staring at the sky and praying for a miracle, or at least a larger window.

Instead, come spring, he got a call from Albert Skiles, a regional architect for the Ozark Institute, a government agency. "Listen, we're planning to sink a little money into a pilot project for the elderly," Skiles said, "and we need you to find a family that will let us build a sunspace on their home. It's a great way to cut down on fuel costs."

It was a terrific idea, except the community didn't want to be bothered. "You couldn't pay me to put one of those things on my house," one man said, closing the door on John.

Even if they didn't want it, he did.

In the next few weeks, he and Skiles designed a structure

John and Colleen pose proudly in front of the new addition they built that helps supply both heat and food. Also part of the crew are Nathan, 8; David, 3; and John-Thomas, one and one-half.

suited to the house's existing southern facade. The old front porch, along with a portion of the exterior wall, could be knocked out and a 14x6-foot sunspace installed in its place. The house's front door could stay where it was. By using asphalt shingles to match the roof, and materials such as pine and tempered glass, the sunspace would look great and to John, that was important. "I wouldn't sacrifice the aesthestics of the way we built the sunspace even for one-third more heating efficiency," he said.

John broke ground in the spring, just about the time Colleen delivered John-Thomas, their third son. He dug below the frost line, securing the foundation trenches with railroad ties and cement.

At night, after work, John constructed the kneewall (the front vertical panel below the glazing) from 2 x 4s. While building the shutters that cover the kneewall, he realized he would have an insulating problem. On winter days the shutters would be opened, allowing the sunlight

28

to strike some type of reflective surface, filter through removable glass panels, and be absorbed by a row of six 55-gallon drums. At night, however, the shutters would be closed to help lock in the day's heat gain. So they should insulate as well as reflect. He took a tip from an Ozark farmer and purchased some inexpensive insulation which had the reflective properties of aluminum foil, and had been used for years to insulate Ozark chicken coops.

For the glazing, John employed the aid of an enterprising friend who scouted out a glass factory just south of Berryville that sold tempered glass at $4 for each of his five 21x64-inch panels. John set the panels in place using strips of pine and Styrofoam. Finally, he tacked sheets of Flex-o-glass plastic to the panel's interior and caulked the edges with silicon to prevent water seepage. On completion, the sunspace was snug, dry and warm.

Of course, too much warmth could be a problem. Although it would be marvelous for cold winter nights, John didn't relish sweltering during the summer. The glass panels were removable in the summer, so there would be a breeze. And to insure a cross-draft, John installed two side-wall vents which were covered with screens in the summer and Styrofoam panels in the winter.

All in all, the cost of materials wasn't astronomical. With the discount on glass, and the use of Styrofoam, plastic and inexpensive chicken coop insulation, the total expense was under $500.

The sunspace was completed in spring of 1978 and sunlight, 48 square feet of it, began pouring into the Strandquist home. That winter, they didn't need their central gas heating system at all. Instead, they relied on the sunspace and an old wood stove for warmth. Even during February, a month when temperatures can dip below zero in the Ozarks, the average temperature in their home hovered near 60° F. As a result, they were now spending an average of $9 on monthly heating bills.

Besides fuel savings, the greenhouse offered other economic advantages. John and Colleen set large wooden planters atop the storage barrels to grow lettuce, radishes and tomatoes. All the garden greens flourished, including a batch of carrot seeds that came up parsley.

The old cement porch floor, now warmed by the storage barrels, became a play area for the children. Colleen stripped off their snowsuits and set the children on the floor as she rifled for dry clothes. She wasn't worried about the children catching cold: the sunspace floor was even warmer than the kitchen.

By this time, neighbors began to ask questions about design, materials and fuel costs. But John doesn't believe everyone will start building sunspaces just yet. "There just isn't any money in the hills," he said. "Even though they'd get their original investment back in three years, it's hard to convince them. They're set in their ways."

Even so, John hopes to begin building sunspaces on commission. One of his first customers will be his once-skeptical mother-in-law. Others will gradually come around, too, John believes. "With gas prices soaring you *need* a sunspace," he said. "That doesn't mean you have to understand completely all the specifics as to how it works. Solar enthusiasts are interested in all the energy rhetoric. I just felt my way along when I built this, and all I can say is, for the first time in our house we can sit in the living room and watch the stars come out."

In New Hampshire: The Colonial Connection

Nancy Meserve crouched by the line of maple trees out front, wishing she were a million miles away, or at least still upstairs sleeping. "Len," she had called to her husband that morning, "don't forget the metal buckets to collect the sap." Len brought out some old plastic milk containers. Nancy groaned. She knew the neighbors would laugh at the slipshod equipment. In their town of Westmoreland, New Hampshire, refining sap was serious business. Farmers made a tidy profit by selling a gallon of maple syrup for upwards of $20. Still, at 6 A.M., there was nothing for Nancy to do but simply use the materials at hand. She would have gladly paid the extra expense of buying syrup in lieu of a little more sleep, but Len was adamant. He liked being self-sufficient, and gathering sap was a good way to start.

As Nancy swung the metal drill into place against the tree, with Len's bandaged hand resting against her knee, she had to smile. There wasn't, for the moment, any place she'd rather be.

Even a layperson can construct a sunspace. "Before I built the greenhouse," Len Meserve confessed, "I had never made anything more complicated than a doghouse and a rabbit hutch." Obviously, Len's humble beginnings didn't prove to be a barrier.

30

"It's the most beautiful combination of the 18th and 20th centuries I could imagine," said one neighbor, describing this sunspace addition. We agree.

their home. Nancy wasn't so sure. Although she didn't like supporting the utility company any more than Len, and in fact refused to use central heating, she had hoped they'd stick to simply using the old wood stove.

She inserted a metal spout into the neatly drilled tree hole. These trees, she thought, were sometimes a lot of trouble. They had almost prevented Len from building their sunspace. Thanks to the maple-lined driveway and front lawn, her husband couldn't select an appropriate sunspace site. Nearly 100 feet tall, the trees shaded the house for a good por-

Of course, she wasn't always so enthusiastic about Len's do-it-yourself projects. Take the time he came home and announced he'd quit his job selling maintenance supplies to begin work on a solar greenhouse. As Len's knowledge of solar power had been limited to sunbathing, the announcement was a shock. Still, she knew he hadn't been the same since reading an article on sunspaces: he became convinced it was the best option for heating

Nancy Meserve doesn't care beans about the extra time and energy she devotes to gardening in the sunspace. The fresh year-round vegetables are worth it.

31

tion of the day, which was a boon in the summertime. But it greatly reduced the amount of solar radiation on the south side of the house, even after the leaves had fallen. Cutting down all the trees was out of the question.

Finally, Len had confided his troubles to a friend. "Why don't you build a sunspace where the old kitchen porch is?" his companion asked. Len examined the facade. By knocking down the porch rafters and tearing up the cement floor, he'd have enough space to construct a 14x22-foot greenhouse. The porch overhead could remain as the sunspace roof. Because the kitchen was on the end of the house farthest from the maples, the sunspace would receive sunlight from 10 A.M. until 2:30 P.M., when the shadows from the upper branches would start crossing the glass in midwinter. Another hour of collection time would have been ideal but not essential.

Unfortunately, the site plan entailed tree-trimming. The top ten feet were shaved from the pine trees out front. Three sugar maples by the driveway were uprooted. Nancy had felt a pang as she watched Len split and cord the tree wood, but now she was glad. After all, it means three less trees to tap.

With the landscaping problems hurdled, Len designed the sunspace. He worked with Nancy at every step to insure the addition would maintain the simplicity of their 18th century Colonial home.

As Nancy continued to tap the trees, she recollected their careful planning. With the help of her father and a few volunteers, Len broke ground in August of 1978. Ruefully, Nancy recalled the neighbors' amazement. Just as they were now stopping by to tease the Meserves about the plastic jug sap collectors, so had they stopped by during the construction of the sunspace. Len, they thought, was nuts to use solar energy in such a cold climate. Even Len's sister-in-law, inspecting the foundation, didn't understand. "What's that you're building," she asked, "a swimming pool?"

Len was undaunted. He loved working outdoors on a challenging project. Besides, he was positive a sunspace would work, even in the sub-zero New Hampshire winters.

"I believe very sincerely that all those calculations for heat loss, roof angles, and thermal mass are nice," Len explained, "but if you really understand the principles behind a sunspace—things like absolutely airtight construction, south face, plenty of insulation, and overhang for summer cooling—then no matter how you do the final details, the greenhouse will work. Each of the principles has wide and forgiving limits."

While Len knew the basic construction limits were flexible, he also knew Nancy's ideas were more rigid. "I was very demanding in terms of aesthetics," she said, "since all we had seen were some greenhouses made with plastic and other cheap-looking materials. I had never seen any thing that I would want attached to my house." As a result, Len planned carefully, with an eye toward the simple, spare, elegant lines of the farmhouse. "We didn't want to lose the view of the front yard and the trees from our kitchen," he added. "I could get Thermopane glass patio door replacements through a friend at half price. That's a standard size, so there really wasn't too much room to play around with for different kneewall heights or roof slopes," he said.

He attached the sunspace through the clapboard wall of the kitchen. A door and two windows were already in that wall, making it easy for the hot air from the sunspace to warm the kitchen. Such access also offered an enjoyable view with early morning coffee.

The greenhouse end-walls were fashioned with some old clapboard he found in the barn. And although Len wanted to cut costs, he and Nancy opted to trim the 150 square feet of glazing with aluminum because it was attractive and required minimal care. All totaled, the cost of materials was $1,700.

During the sunspace's first winter, Len noticed a substantial fuel savings.

"In the fall and again in the spring, the edges of the cold season, the greenhouse really benefits the home," he said. "Starting at the end of February, we don't need a wood fire at all in the kitchen, except maybe a small one on a really cold evening. In fact, in February we had 11 days in a row below zero, but the days were bright and the greenhouse didn't come close to freezing."

Len didn't return to selling maintenance supplies until the sunspace was completed, so saving money was imperative. The Meserves conserved wisely, shutting the windows and doors to the greenhouse on winter nights. Because of the heating contribution the sunspace made in the fall and early spring, they saved more than one cord of

Low, screened vent at one end of the greenhouse provides entry of cool summer ventilation and permits warm air to escape through a higher-positioned vent at the greenhouse's opposite end.

wood. With the money accrued, they established a bank account to buy insulation for the entire house for next year.

The greenhouse really had been a good money-saving incentive, Nancy thought, as she trudged toward the barn with the sap. She set the mixture to boiling, knowing it would be hours before they distilled one gallon of pure syrup. She realized few people would go to such great lengths to save money but Len was different. He insisted upon using homegrown produce rather than foodstuffs from distributors, and the sunspace provides them with all the year-round fresh vegetables they need. Twelve 55-gallon water drums, set under the planting beds, keep the soil at an average temperature of 50° F, even when outside temperatures dip to 30 below.

"To us, the real value of the sunspace turned out to be its ability to produce food," Len said. "The food it gives us is of the nicest quality. In the dead of winter, it's very satisfying to be able to work with green growing things, to be sitting down at the table and having the smell of greenhouse air come in. On a sunny day, we come out to the sunspace to sit or read. You just have no idea how important it is if you live with a really cold, long winter to be looking out the window from your table at beautiful, lush foliage—that's edible!"

Nancy had to agree. Winter is a monotonous season, and any small gift, like the smell of green-

ery, is savored: so is sap-gathering in February. She and Len huddled under a blanket in the barn, tasting the sap as it melted down to sweet syrup.

Once again, Len's enthusiasm had been founded in fact. Even though the sunspace and maple-sugar-gathering entailed some extra work, there was something to be said for maintaining one's personal independence. Besides, by taking the time to initiate new projects, you inspire others. In fact, after Len built the sunspace, two members

Fifty-five gallon water-filled drums absorb daytime heat and release it at night; keeping the garden beds from freezing during cold New England nights.

of the local school board followed suit. And who knows? Maybe some other community residents will begin splitting their own wood, harvesting their own food and distilling their own syrup.

But not at six in the morning.

Building It for Yourself

PART I: MAJOR DECISIONS TO MAKE

Let's not kid ourselves: this is a hefty project. You're not going to get it done in a weekend—although many a sunspace has been raised by weekend workshops of two dozen people and leaders who know exactly what they're doing.

Most of us don't. We need to sit down beforehand and think things through. And we need a set of plans. If we don't sketch out at least a crude blueprint, wherein all angles and dimensions fall happily together, we're looking for trouble.

A sunspace will dramatically change the exterior of your home . . . for the better, if you do things right. You'll want to convince yourself (as well as a spouse, probably) that the new addition will be attractive, comfortable, worth the money and properly done.

So consider this:

Purpose

What are you going to do with it? Are you looking forward to a new place in the house to spend time in? Alone or with the family? Are you dreaming of picking your salad ten minutes before dinner every night? Or are you mainly interested in reducing your high fuel bill?

Two roads diverge here. You can take the low-temperature-swing road, or the high-temperature-swing road.

If indoor gardening is your vision, you want to take the low road. Your tender crops would be wiped out by a dead-of-winter fluctuation from 90° by day to near-freezing lows at night. Fairly steady temperatures can be maintained by these methods, alone or in combination: (1) indoor thermal shutters or a special interior curtain that tightly covers the glass at night to cut heat loss; (2) thermal mass to soak up sunlight and radiate it back as heat at night; (3) letting some of your nighttime house heat drift into the sunspace . . . frankly, a terrible idea if done without step 1.

Taking the high road means you don't care what kind of daytime highs and nighttime lows you get in your sunspace. You shut it off tightly from the house at night, and you won't worry about plants freezing their buds off. You simply want a daytime heat collector.

This distinction is a key one. If you want to keep plants alive, you're going to have to store some of the solar energy you collect; which means you're going to have to have an attached solar greenhouse. The heat you store to maintain your plants at night is heat that never finds its way into the rest of the house. A daytime heat collector moves all of its heat into the house, leaving no stored heat for itself at night.

Having made your choice of priorities, you now have a handle on designing your sunspace.

Thermal Dynamics for Plants

If you're going to produce food, you'll want to incorporate thermal mass. The floor should be of earth, concrete, stone or brick. Insulate its perimeter so heat doesn't migrate into the ground. Design your glazing so as much sun as possible strikes the floor directly.

You could also put thermal mass along the vertical inner wall—the wall that was previously the exterior of your house. If your exterior is already brick or stone, you're golden. If not, a common solution is to stack 55-gallon drums full of water on the back wall. Paint the drums black for better heat absorption. If black is too dismal for you, dark blue barrels are a mere five percent less efficient, and red barrels sacrifice only nine percent.

Getting the midday sun (10 A.M. to 2 P.M.) to strike the barrels directly means you'll be getting four times as much energy absorbed by the mass rather than as a setup in which they merely sit in the hot shade.

How many barrels do you need? According to Edward Mazria's *Passive Solar Energy Book* (Rodale Press, 1979) matching one cubic foot of water (7½ gallons) to every square foot of glazing will result in a temperature swing as small as 15 degrees. That's about 14 drums for 100 square feet of glass.

Adding heat-storing mass to your sunspace moderates the temperature both ways. It holds down daytime highs as well as eases nighttime lows. It performs its thermal give-and-take only within the sunspace unless you pull out your frame wall and make the mass storage the common wall between sunspace and house. That usually presents a situation of major structural change.

Thermal Dynamics for Heat

By comparison, a walk-in daytime solar collector seems like simplicity itself. Your main concern is how to deliver your new heat to the rest of your house. You can get the heat to move itself, or you can give it a little shove.

Getting the heat to move itself means setting up a convective loop. You have to get cool house air entering at the bottom of the sunspace, and solar-heated air flowing out the top. Existing windows and (better yet) doors within the area to be enclosed may provide enough room for air flow. Otherwise you could install a patio door or vents to the house from the top of the sunspace.

If you're planning a two-story sunspace, you should take advantage of its height. Because warm air rises, the warmest air in your sunspace will rise to the

How to Find the Sun

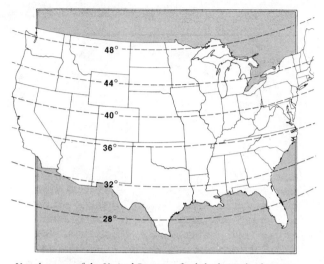

Use the map of the United States to find the latitude closest to your location. Then consult the appropriate sun chart. Each line on the chart traces the sun's path on the 21st day of the two months indicated. The lines make a composite picture of what you would see if you looked due south and stared at the sky for a year.

Here's a hypothetical problem: you live in Kansas City, you're planning a sunspace, but there's a neighbor's house to the left of your site. Will it shade you in winter? With your protractor you determine the house to be about 30 degrees to the east of south, and its roof ridge is 20 degrees above the horizon. The sun chart for 40 degrees North Latitude tells you the sun will rise over your neighbor's roof ridge at 9:30 A.M. on Nov. 21 and Jan. 21, and at 10 A.M. on Dec. 21. So you're in the clear.

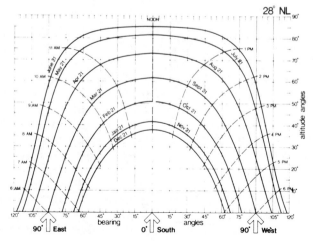

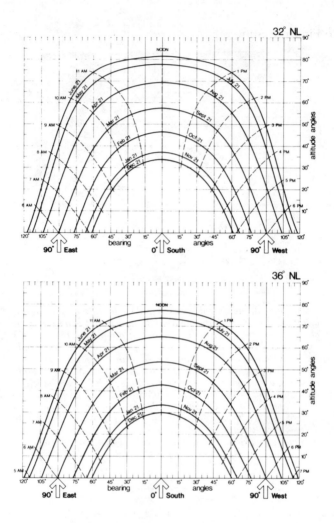

top and into the house through open second-story windows. Cool air from the cellar or first floor will flow into the sunspace, and you will have yourself a powerful convective loop.

Site

The sun is much more predictable than the behavior of big oil powers, but you're still at its mercy. You have to put your sun-space where it gets the most sun and minimal shade. Therefore, find the south side of your house. South is where the sun is. Every day at noon, right on the money.

Chances are very slim you have one wall of your house facing due south. The home building industry is only beginning to inch its way into the solar age by thinking about house plans in relation to the sun. But don't

FIG. C

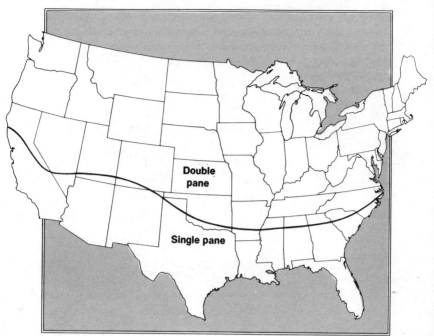

Double pane

Single pane

worry: the performance of a sunspace will suffer by only ten percent if it faces as much as 30 degrees to the east of south or as much as 40 degrees to the west. So you shouldn't have too much trouble getting enough sun. Now let's worry about shade.

Because of the earth's wobbly rotation on its axis, the sun runs along different courses in the sky from one season to the next. It's highest in the southern sky at noon June 21 and lowest at noon on December 21. On that darkest day of the year it climbs to 37 degrees above the horizon if you live in New Orleans; it gets up to only 20 degrees if you live in northern Minnesota.

Here's another simple rule of thumb from Edward Mazria's book. Roughly 90 percent of the sun's energy on a winter day will fall between the hours of 9 A.M. and 3 P.M. The sun is 45 degrees to the east of south at 9 A.M., and 45 degrees to the west of south at 3 P.M.

Make sure the sun gets a full shot at your sunspace during those hours. To do that, you'll need to measure the sun's altitude—its height off the horizon in degrees. That calls for a device that sounds suspiciously jerry-rigged but is perfectly accurate for our purposes. Buy a cheap plastic protractor, drill a hole in it as shown in Figure A, and tie some thread in the hole. Tie washers to the other end. The thread will cross the degree mark that describes the protractor's

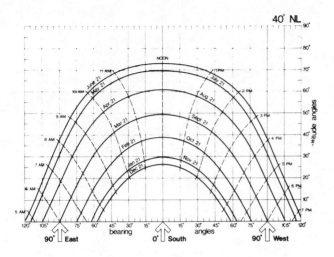

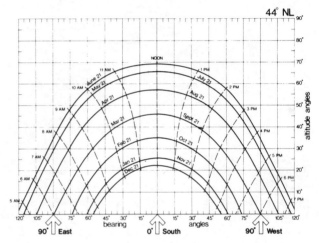

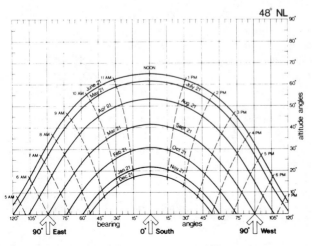

40

Chart 1: Sunspace Shapes

Shape	Relative Cost	Winter Performance	Summer Performance	Head Room	Heating Cost	Window Insulation
	Low	Excellent	Overheats	Poor	Low	Very difficult
	Low	Poor	No light for plants	Excellent	Medium	Easy
	Low	Excellent	Overheats	Fair	Low	Difficult
	Low	Very good	Good	Good	Low	Fairly easy
	Medium—High	Excellent	Overheats	Good	Medium	Very difficult
	Medium	Good	Fair	Excellent	Low	Easy

tilt. That tilt is the sun's altitude.

Now refer to the charts titled "How to Find the Sun" to figure out the sun's path at your latitude. Know its high and low points in degrees during the crucial six hours. Stand where your glazing will be. Run your eye along the straight edge of the protractor tilted at the appropriate angle for each point between 45 degrees east of south to 45 degrees west. Is there anything between your eye and the sky at any of these points? Then you're going to get shade. Hopefully you won't have to ask your neighbor to move his house.

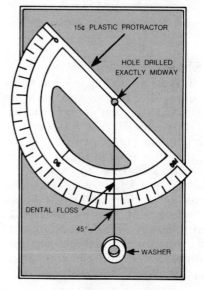

Figure A: Makeshift altitude gauge

Assuming equal sunshine all along your south-facing wall, where do you want to put your sunspace? Where it's easiest. Ideally, you should enclose a door and at least one window. That way you won't have to re-route pipes and wires to make access. Also, think about what rooms you want to heat, and how you can get the warm air to loop through your house and back to the sunspace again. Figure B makes a suggestion.

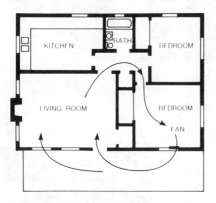

Figure B: Loop the warm air through your house.

Shape

You're making a wintertime heat collector, so you want to aim it at the winter sun head-on. The standard rule has been to angle the glazed wall at 15 degrees plus your latitude.

Don't take it to extremes. I heard of a fellow who read that rule somewhere and spent weeks angling all his glazing wall studs at precisely 57½ degrees. In fact, if you are assured of constant snow cover outside your sunspace, you'll probably gain at least as much solar radiation with a perfectly vertical wall as with a 60-degree wall, because the 90-degree wall picks up reflection off the snow.

If you're living well inside the sunbelt, where snow is rare and the winter sun is higher, you're better off sloping your glazing closer to 45 degrees. There are other considerations to take into account before choosing a shape, and Chart #1 can help.

Size

For everyone north of the sunbelt, my advice is this: make your sunspace as big as you can.

Houses in mild climates, especially small houses, can overheat on sunny winter days if a big sunspace is simmering away at anything near peak efficiency. Maybe you think that's the cat's meow. What a thrill to come home at dusk in early February and have to throw open some windows. If you don't like it, you can always start rolling in black-painted 55-gallon drums of water to soak up some of the heat.

Which brings up a crucial design factor: summer performance. If you have thermal mass on the back wall, you want to keep the high summer sun off it, so you want enough of a roof to do just that. If you don't have thermal mass, think about either (a) covering the glazing, or (b) venting the excess heat.

Glazing can be covered by the same indoor insulating shutters that keep the heat *in* on cold winter nights. To reflect summer heat, they should have a foil face toward the sun. Or you can rig up, say, bamboo curtains inside or out to shade the space.

Heat can be vented through a door on the side of the sunspace or through vents at the top of the glazing. Some sunspaces have their uppermost glazing panels fold outward for summer cooling. That's an appropriate alternative in temperate climates, but such fixtures usually seal poorly and, as a result, leak loads of heat in northern climes.

How much heat can you harness? Will the sun kick in for a third of your fuel needs? Two-thirds? It's tough to say. There are so many variables . . . like whether you live in Buffalo or Sante Fe, and have dreary cloudy winter days or bright sunny ones. How much insulation are you going to put in the walls and ceiling and around the foundation? Are you going to use single or double glazing? How big should it be? Do you want thermal mass? How is it going to connect with the house? How big is your house? You get the idea. Everybody's sunspace is different. To find how much heat can be gathered by several variations of glazing and climate, see Chart #2.

A final note: Don't think glazing on the east and west walls of the sunspace produce as much heat as south-facing glass.

Chart 2: The Sun Pours in Like Heating Oil

	APPROXIMATE NET CLEAR DAY BTU GAINS*			GALLONS #2 FUEL OIL SAVED PER CLEAR DAY**			POTENTIAL DOLLAR SAVINGS PER WINTER***		
	100 sf	150 sf	200 sf						
	A	B	C	A	B	C	A	B	C
Atlanta, GA	215,125	322,678	430,250	2.23	3.33	4.44	$307	$458	$612
Nashville, TN	211,750	317,625	423,500	2.15	3.23	4.32	$280	$421	$564
Dodge City, KS	208,125	312,188	416,250	2.05	3.07	4.10	$342	$511	$684
Columbus, OH	204,000	306,000	408,000	1.96	2.96	3.95	$227	$343	$458
El Paso, TX	218,250	327,375	436,500	2.27	3.40	4.54	$433	$649	$867
Greensboro, NC	211,750	317,625	423,500	2.14	3.21	4.29	$284	$426	$570
Boston, MA	199,875	299,813	399,750	1.93	2.90	3.87	$247	$371	$496
Boise, ID	195,875	293,813	391,750	1.89	2.83	3.77	$251	$376	$501
Bismarck, ND	189,500	284,250	379,000	1.68	2.52	3.36	$223	$334	$447
Great Falls, MT	182,875	274,312	365,750	1.67	2.50	3.34	$222	$332	$444
Las Vegas, NV	211,750	317,625	423,500	2.21	3.31	4.41	$427	$640	$853
Portland, ME	195,875	293,812	391,750	1.82	2.73	3.63	$206	$310	$410
Los Angeles, CA	215,125	322,687	430,250	2.28	3.43	4.57	$396	$597	$795
Rapid City, SD	195,875	293,812	391,750	1.82	2.73	3.64	$268	$402	$536
Tucson, AR	218,250	327,375	436,500	2.33	3.49	4.65	$478	$717	$956

*These columns show how much heat energy in Btus a well-made sunspace with a) 100, b) 150, or c) 200 square feet of collection area will produce on a clear winter day. Night heat losses are allowed for. Loose construction or single glazing will lower heat gains; night shutters or extra insulation will increase heat retention.
**If you use natural gas, divide Btu figures in the first columns by 750 to find savings in cubic feet. For electricity, divide by 3,410 for savings in kilowatt-hours. For 1pg, divide by 68,250 for gallons. Furnace efficiency is allowed for.
***Costs are figured at $1 per gallon. Normal winter cloudiness is allowed for. Severe conditions will lower these figures, which are ballpark estimates. Mild weather may raise dollar savings even higher.

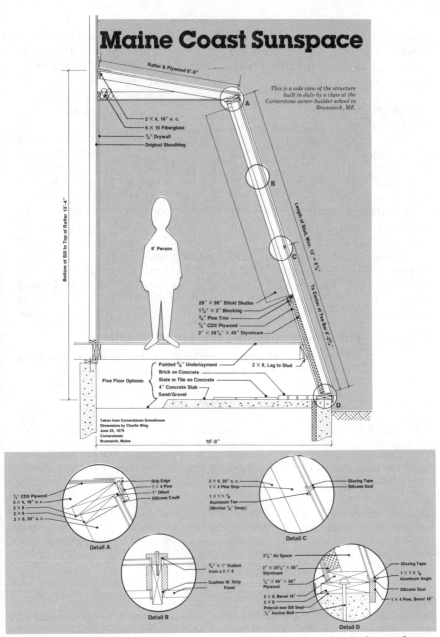

Maine Coast Sunspace

Rafter & Plywood 6'-0"

This is a side view of the structure built in July by a class at the Cornerstone owner-builder school in Brunswick, ME.

2 × 4, 16" o. c.
6 × 15 Fiberglass
½" Drywall
Original Sheathing

Bottom of Sill to Top of Rafter 13'-4"

6' Person

Length of Stud, Max. 12' = 6'½"

To Center of Tee Bar 6'-2½"

28" × 96" Bifold Shutter
1½" × 2" Blocking
¾" Pine Trim
½" CDX Plywood
2" × 28½" × 48" Styrofoam

Painted ⅝" Underlayment
Brick on Concrete
Slate or Tile on Concrete
4" Concrete Slab
Sand/Gravel

Five Floor Options:

2 × 6, Lag to Stud

Taken from Cornerstones Greenhouse
Dimensions by Charlie Wing
June 25, 1979
Cornerstones
Brunswick, Maine

10'-0"

Detail A
½" CDX Plywood
2 × 4, 16" o. c.
2 × 8
2 × 6
2 × 6, 30" o. c.
Drip Edge
1 × 4 Pine
1" Offset
Silicone Caulk

Detail C
2 × 6, 30" o. c.
1 × 4 Pine Stop
1 × 1 × ⅛ Aluminum Tee (Mortise ⅛" Deep)
Glazing Tape
Silicone Seal

Detail B
⅜" × 1" Rabbet from a 2 × 4
Cushion W. Strip
Panel

Detail D
3½" Air Space
2" × 28½" × 48" Styrofoam
½" × 48" × 90" Plywood
2 × 8, Bevel 18"
2 × 8
Polycal-one Sill Seal
½" Anchor Bolt
Glazing Tape
1 × 1 × ⅛ Aluminum Angle
Silicone Seal
1 × 4 Pine, Bevel 18"

In winter, they probably lose a little more heat than they gain, and in summer they cause overheating. If you're planning on plants, provide enough light-colored surface on the inside wall to diffuse the light. Otherwise your greenery will lean southward.

Glazings

Although an abundance of

new glazing materials is emerging from solar manufacturers, glass is still the favorite. It's more expensive than most, but it's the most handsome and longest-lasting of your choices. It's also the easiest to obtain.

Consult the map of the United States in Figure C to see whether you need one or two layers of glazing. If you live in the land of single panes you can buy sheets of tempered low-iron "water-white" glass for around $1 per square foot. The low-iron content gives it the greatest solar transmittance of all types of glass: 91 percent of the sun's energy gets through it.

If you need double-glazing, standard-sized tempered Thermopane patio door units are the best choice. The most common size is 34 x 76 inches. It's available from local glass outlets for about $3.50 per square foot, which puts you close to $70 per unit. Shop around.

The second most common glazing material is fiberglass-reinforced plastic (FRP) sheeting. It's made in rolls of 4 and 5 feet in width, but can be cut and drilled to fit any situation. Although it's not transparent, the solar transmittance is only slightly less than low-iron glass.

The main disadvantage of FRP sheeting is that it may turn yellow with age. Exactly how long it will hold up without yellowing may depend upon the individual brand. We can't give you firm advice on this; all we can say is what happened to us. We put a popular brand of FRP sheeting on a freestanding solar greenhouse at the Rodale Press experimental farm. After four years it turned the color of an old tobacco smoker's teeth. Also, the discoloration caused a 20 percent decrease in solar transmittance, our tests showed.

On the other hand, FRP sheeting now being sold may be "new and improved." Check for manufacturer's claim or (better yet) guarantee on this point. Otherwise you run the risk of doing something you'll kick yourself for later.

Polycarbonate sheeting is a rigid double-wall glazing. Like the FRP sheets, however, it's susceptible to degradation with age. Brand names are Tuffak-Twinwal, Acrylite and Cyrolon.

There are plastic films such as Tedlar, Teflon and Mylar. They are too flimsy to be used as your sole glazing. Their best application is as the second layer of glazing inside glass or FRP sheets. They cost considerably less than $1 per square foot.

These varieties of plastic glazings have their staunch supporters. They say plastics weigh much less than glass; thus, are cheaper to ship, easier to carry, and don't require heavy framing lumber: 2 x 4s will do. There's no danger of breakage during installation. They can be cut to fit odd places, or trimmed to fit miscalculations in framing. They're more forgiving of an amateur's errors, in other words. And heavy hail or flying hardballs are less worrisome.

But they may take some hunting to find a nearby source. Try the yellow pages in your telephone directory for energy stores or solar contractors.

Final note: it is supremely important to choose glazing *before* you order lumber and build the frame, because most likely you'll be spacing the studs to accommodate standard sizes. Cost of glazing probably will be half your total budget.

PART II: PUTTING IT TOGETHER

Last summer I joined in a one-week course on sunspace construction given by Cornerstones, a school in Brunswick, Maine, that devotes itself mostly to teaching people how to build their own energy-efficient homes. Our class built the frame and installed the glazing on a large sunspace facing the sea. Some of its details are worthy of imitation, especially if you want to build something of quality. "There are hundreds of solar greenhouses around now that will be gone in ten years," said crew leader John Lyons. "This one should last the life of the house."

The foundation had been poured before we arrived at the construction site. It didn't do us any favors. Whoever dealt with the foundation contractor forgot to specify 2 inches of rigid blue Styrofoam insulation boards along the outside perimeter. So we had to dig around it, adhere the boards to the cement with adhesive and backfill again.

If you have your foundation contracted out, be sure to specify perimeter insulation to a depth below the frost line: three to five feet in northern climes. Also, be specific about where he should place the anchor bolts. They should pop through the sills between wall studs, not right under one. The spacing of your framing members is determined by the type of glazing you choose.

The sill is the long board where frame joins foundation. Because our sunspace had a south wall more than 24 feet long, we needed two lengths of 2 x 8s to span the distance. To insure a tight seal we lap-jointed them. The lap joints (Figure D) were made by cutting halfway into the board across the grain at tight intervals with a circular saw, then chiseling out the required space.

Once that was done, the sill boards were laid in place over the anchor bolts and smacked with a hammer so the bolts would make a mark. At those marks we drilled holes for the bolts to pass through.

When the sill finally rested in place, we pried it up in order to put an 8-inch-wide roll of fiberglass insulation between sill and foundation. Then we put the

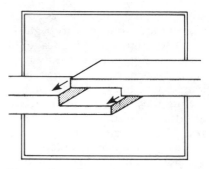

Figure D: A lap joint

46

sill back and bolted it down.

We treated all joints and ends of all framing members with the wood preservative Cuprinol. Beware of creosote and "penta" (pentachlorophenol) preservatives. They're bad for plants and people, according to federal government reports. Cuprinol is an added protection against moisture, and moisture can overflow in a space used to grow plants 100 feet from the Atlantic on a coastline that loves to shroud itself in melancholy fogs.

The frame of the south wall was built as a unit—bottom plate, top plate and studs—flat on the grass in front of the site. The wall was designed to be at a 72-degree tilt, so we had to cut the bottom ends of each stud at the same 18-degree angle. The 2 x 8 bottom plate also needed an 18-degree bevel in order to provide a straight line down to the sill (see detail "D"). Top ends of the studs were left square and fastened to a 2 x 6 top plate.

In sawing the studs, we labored to get one perfect, then used it as the template for the others and took the pencil line with us as we cut.

With our framing members cut to plan, we laid them out on the grass in the shape they would soon assume. On the bottom plate we measured off precisely where the center of each stud should fall—every 30 inches, in our case—then measured ¾-inch to either side (framing lumber is 1½ inches thick) and drew a line across the grain. The stud would fall between the lines. We marked off corresponding lines on the top plate by using the bottom as a template.

As with the sill, the span was too great for a single board to comprise the bottom and top plate. So we butt-jointed two boards at exactly the center of a stud, taking care that the same stud did not have butt joints on top and bottom. When we nailed the plates to the studs, the butt joint studs got six nails pounded into their end, instead of three.

To temporarily reinforce the butt joints for the stress of raising the wall, we nailed a scrap piece of plywood across the top plate joint to act as a brace. Then we lifted the wall into a vertical position, heaved, carried and shouted it into place. Up where the studs met the top plate, little tufts of grass were sticking from the joints, betraying its earthbound beginnings.

With the wall firmly braced, measuring tapes were hauled out and draped everywhere to insure that the numbers on the blueprints had been rightly transformed into the reality of the wood. A tape was stretched midway between the top and bottom plates to be sure that the studs are all spaced at 30 inches. Of course they weren't. Errant members got whacked into position by "toeing in" nails where the studs meet the bottom plate.

Having the glazing wall up was like having the key pieces of a puzzle in place. The remaining framing was denouement. One member of the class, a Nova Scotia carpenter named Terry Fuller, whipped together the end wall in jig-time. Roof rafters were angled and, more often, cut to the demands of the space rather than the dimension on the plans.

The floor and ceiling joists were hung from metal joist hangers nailed to ledger strips at either end. Ledger strips were made level by holding a long board in place, placing a level on it and then "snapping a line" of chalked string. (In floor and ceiling joists, leveling is everything. You find that out in a hurry when you come to nail down the plywood and nail up the drywall.)

Once all the framing is up, you're ready to do the glazing. The glazing details on this sunspace are something to be admired, because they know what to do with rainwater: get rid of it. I've seen some wood and fiberglass sunspaces in which each glazing panel has a natural little trough at its bottom edge. A few years of rain sitting in those troughs brings a case of dry rot.

The glazing in this sunspace is tempered Thermopane. Each unit measures ¾ x 28 x 76 inches. Every inch of its perimeter sits on Butyl glazing tape, which in turn sits on ⅛ x 1 x 1-inch aluminum angles (horizontal edges) and ¾ x 2-inch pine stops (vertical edges) nailed to both sides of the wall studs.

Note: before you do anything with the aluminum angles, rub them with steel wool and wipe them with acetone to remove the manufacturer's oil. Otherwise the Butyl glazing tape might not stick.

To install the bottommost angle, rout the bottom plate ⅛-inch deep. Lay the aluminum into its snug berth, and drill holes for brass screws every 12 inches. Before screwing down, start 6-inch aluminum flashing at the top of the rout and then screw through the flashing. This will really keep your sill dry.

We also routed out a spot in the middle of the wall studs for the aluminum tee that separates the bottom and top tiers of Thermopane units (detail "C"). Glazing tape is laid along the top edge of the tee's protrusion, and a bead of silicone caulk goes underneath.

Once all the Thermopane units were resting quietly in their Butyl beds, they were held in place by rabbeted vertical batten strips screwed to the studs (detail "B").

There are thousands of construction details I've not mentioned or merely touched upon. To tell you everything would take a book. If you get stumped and have no handy neighbors or friends, call in a carpenter for a look-see. By all means, seek advice.

Despite the best-laid plans, things go wrong. No matter how much we measured and remeasured as we went along, the wood defied us. We did so many things over again: a door was 6 inches too low and had to be raised, joist hangers were pulled off and reset, rafters were shimmed. "This is a course in sunspace *disassembly*," class member Scott Hicks lamented at one point.

But our job got done, and done well. So will yours.

WALLS OF WARM AIR

*This do-it-yourself device
turns a chilly house wall
into a solar collector.*

By the looks of early spring, winter in northern Nebraska must be as tough as the best of them. The muddy brown landscape has been flattened by snows and bitter winds, and farmers await warmer weather before bringing out their tractors and seeds. So winter is a time that northern Nebraskans just want to "get through." The snowbound farmers pass the time tending livestock, going over equipment and, of course, keeping warm.

The Stark's collector. The tree stump in the foreground is the mark of a dedicated solarizer. It was an evergreen that would have shaded the collector. It had to go.

It never used to take much to stay warm, but lately the prices of fuel oil and propane have been climbing above the cornstalks. The current 20 to 50 percent annual increases in energy costs make a farmer's net gains, if he's lucky enough to have any, noticeably slimmer; enough to make saving energy worth thinking about.

Enter the Small Farm Energy Project and, among other items, their solar wall air-heating collector. SFEP (P.O. Box 736, Hartington, NB 68739) is a nonprofit assistance group formed to help small farmers, already threatened by taxes, agribusiness and inflation, to reduce farm energy use. The wall collector is one of several solar and conservation options the SFEP has made available to farmers. It has proven itself to be effective without being expensive.

We'll look at two different collectors installed by farmers on their houses, in enough detail so you can build one for yourself. The collector at Paul Phelps' house is small—120 square feet—and provides direct heating from collector to house. The other collector was built by Ken and Jan Stark and has nearly twice the surface area—220 square feet—of the Phelps system. The Stark collector is large enough to require a more round-about air flow pattern than the Phelps straight-through design, and also to warrant the addition of a heat storage component, in the form of small stones, to make better use of the larger amounts of Btus produced.

Before Paul Phelps built his collector, he knew what he wanted in a solar system: "Something that doesn't look funny and isn't sophisticated. You know, the worst place to have sophisticated machines is on a farm." Eight years ago he traded being an industrial engineer in Chicago for 480 acres and a run-down farmstead. He's been "busier than heck ever since," and he loves it, seven days a week.

With the farm's original old, gray farmhouse sagging serenely into oblivion, Paul's first big project was to build a new home. His wife, Wilma, was chief designer, and she allowed her pencil and ruler to be guided by her intuition. The result was a house built with a broad south face that framed a generous window area for passive space heating. "When we come around to the winter solstice," said Paul, "the sunlight makes it all the way back to the fireplace wall. And that's a few ton of stones getting heated."

The Phelps' System

The solar wall collector was added in the fall of 1978, and it easily passed Paul's ruling against complexity and weird looks. Simple it is. A look at its cross section shows it to be your basic solar heat collector: a box with a blackened metal absorber covered by a light-admitting, heat-trapping glazing material. In true collector form the unit receives radiant light energy through the glazing, and when the light strikes the absorber it becomes infrared heat. Because the glazing admits sunlight while blocking the outward passage of infrared, the temperature inside the collector climbs much higher than outside air temperature. Given enough sunshine, these collectors can reach 200° F and higher, if there's no air movement through it. When the heat transferring fluid—air or water—stops moving through a collector and just sits there, a collector in that condition is called "stagnant."

But air flow is what heats the house: a thermostatically controlled blower of a calculated

The Phelps' Collector

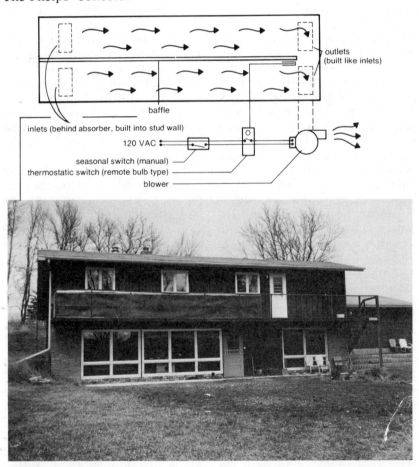

The Phelps' collector. You can make a solar wall fit just about anywhere. The Phelps like this one so much, they've added another unit on the same wall to the right of the doorway.

size pulls cooler room air in from one end of the collector and blows it out the other. For best efficiency, the air moves behind the absorber; between it and the building siding, while a dead air space is maintained in the absorber-glazing gap. The heat building up in the collector migrates to and heats up the passing room air, which emerges at the collector outlet 30 to 50 degrees hotter than it was at the inlet.

Simple as it sounds, that's about all there is to air-heating collectors, and you're not going to get bombarded with a string of *ands*, *ifs* or *buts* that would turn this design into a beast of complicated technicality. The solar wall collector is, by all means, a well-ripened, do-it-yourself solar retrofit option, but it didn't mature by being some "trickle-down" technological child of NASA or the Department of Defense. Quite the contrary, this design has evolved from the work of several grass roots organizations like the Energy Project, groups like the Domestic Technology Institute, the San Luis Valley (Colorado) Solar Energy Association and various Community Action Project (CAP) groups. Working independently and through the solar grapevine these groups have developed and refined a good idea into a workable assemblage of lumber and hardware accompanied by a set of design and operation guidelines that makes it possible for the good idea to be applied to meet part of the space heating requirement of just about any style of wood-frame building that has a favorable solar aspect of within 30 degrees east or west of true south.

These guidelines, worked out by calculation plus trial and error, make the difference between the success of an optimized system and the question mark of a botched job. Often, you can't tell whether a system is botched; you get heat, but less than you should.

As the photograph of the Phelps collector shows, there was not much space available for locating the collector; so much of the south wall had already been spoken for in windows and doors. Paul's aim for simplicity was held intact by not building the collector around any windows, although the building's heating load could certainly use the output of the extra collector area. In fact, the Phelps have recently added another 66 square feet of collector in a separate system built to the left of the porch door.

The horizontal shape of the collector naturally called for a simple, end-to-end air flow from inlet to outlet. As the operating diagram shows, the "duct work" (holes in the wall with the cavities formed by Sheetrock, wall-studs and siding) forms inlet and outlet vents at both ends of the collector. The blower is located at the collector outlet. From the outlet warm air is blown into rooms on the lower floor. Room air is therefore "sucked" rather than pushed through the collector.

There is good reason for this configuration: the collector operates at a negative pressure, and were there any air leaks to the outside, cold air would be drawn into the unit where it would be heated. If the blower were at the inlet, the collector would be pressurized, and any leakage would send valuable hot air to the outside. All in all it's a small but important detail, and hopefully it will never be useful. The goal of construction is to end up with zero leakage. That goal is realized by thinking "seal, seal, seal" every step of the way to completion.

Building a Collector

The first step is to build the collector perimeter and develop the proper air flow gap. The shallow depth of this gap is easily calculated. It depends on the variables of collector size, air volume flow rate (cubic feet per minute, "cfm") and air velocity (feet per minute, "fpm"). (You'll find more information in the box

The Stark Collector

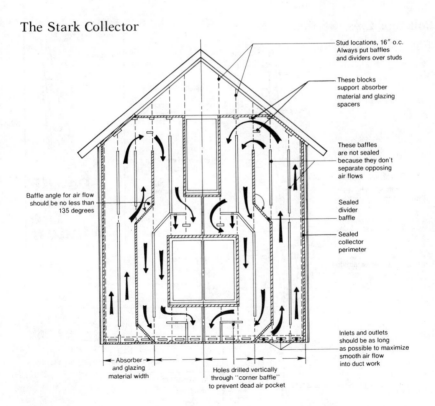

Stud locations, 16" o.c. Always put baffles and dividers over studs

These blocks support absorber material and glazing spacers

These baffles are not sealed because they don't separate opposing air flows

Sealed divider baffle

Sealed collector perimeter

Baffle angle for air flow should be no less than 135 degrees

Inlets and outlets should be as long as possible to maximize smooth air flow into duct work

Absorber and glazing material width

Holes drilled vertically through "corner baffle" to prevent dead air pocket of guidelines.) In the Phelps case the gap was determined to be 1¼ inches and wood strips for the perimeter were cut accordingly, given a bead of caulking on one side and nailed through the siding to the wall studs. This collector's one and only horizontal baffle is also placed at this time. Baffles in these collectors are used to maintain proper air flow and direction.

The absorber material generally used is corrugated metal roofing, either galvanized steel or aluminum that is painted at the site or has a factory-baked enamel finish. Aluminum, being about twice as effective as steel at conducting heat, is the better choice, though it may be more expensive if bought new. The absorber sheets are cut so that the corrugations run perpendicular to the direction of air flow. The thought here is that more turbulence is created if air is blown across the ripples of the absorber, which increases the extraction of heat. Once again, small matters that make a difference.

Before the absorber is installed it must be painted, on *both* sides. Flat black is always

Collector Cross Section

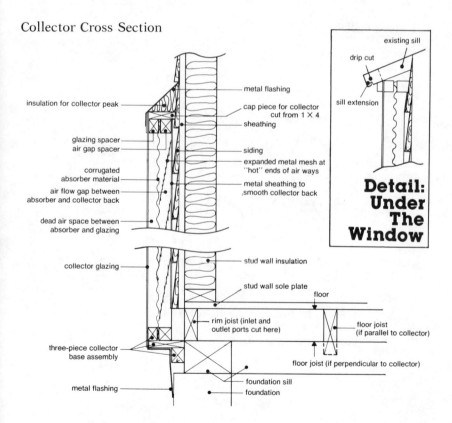

insulation for collector peak

glazing spacer
air gap spacer

corrugated
absorber material

air flow gap between
absorber and collector back

dead air space between
absorber and glazing

collector glazing

three-piece collector
base assembly

metal flashing

metal flashing
cap piece for collector
cut from 1 × 4
sheathing

siding
expanded metal mesh at
"hot" ends of air ways
metal sheathing to
smooth collector back

stud wall insulation

stud wall sole plate
floor

rim joist (inlet and
outlet ports cut here)

foundation sill
foundation

floor joist
(if parallel to collector)

floor joist (if perpendicular to collector)

existing sill
drip cut

sill extension

**Detail:
Under
The
Window**

54

the optimum color for heat collection, but you will sacrifice just a few percentage points of efficiency if you prefer to show the world a dark brown or dark red or whatever dark color better complements your house. In any case, the inside face of the absorber can be painted black.

Why paint the inside that never sees the light of day? It's interesting: just as flat black is an excellent absorber of solar energy, so too is it an excellent radiator of heat. Thus a black inside absorber surface releases heat conducted from the sunny front side better than the shiny metal surface of the stock material. (And that's a lesson for people with hot water radiators: your white or silver-painted cast iron radiators may look nice, but a dark one gives off more heat.)

Painting the absorber isn't just painting. Proper surface preparation and priming is essential for good paint adhesion and long life in an environment that may experience temperature swings of more than 200 degrees. Surface prep begins with a solvent such as paint thinner or acetone to remove residual oils deposited during manufacturing. This is followed by a washing with detergent and then surface etching with vinegar or muriatic acid or a commercially available etching agent to help adhere the paint. The first coat of paint is a primer coat, so use a standard paint made for just that purpose. For the flat finish coat an oil- or acrylic-base high temperature (300 to 400° F) paint is prefera-ble, sprayed on to obtain an even, thin coating. If you use a roofing material with a baked enamel finish, any glossiness must be lightly sanded away or dulled with liquid sandpaper prior to applying the finish coat. Keep to these practices!, warns the SFEP. They've been learned the hard way by having to strip off glazing and sandblast and repaint blistered, flaked-out absorber.

Because roofing material comes in widths of four feet at most, it has to be joined and sealed wherever edges meet. The Energy Project has been successful with a combination of pop rivets for the mechanical link and a high grade caulking, such as black silicone, for the air seal. Mounting the absorber begins with its attachment to the baffles, to which it also must be sealed. A seal between flat wood and wavy metal is accomplished by using foam strips that come in a standard 1 x 1-inch dimension. The seals around the perimeter call for more caulking on flat edges and again for the foam strips on the rippled edges. It's also possible to obtain wood and neoprene strips that are precut to match the profile of the absorber's corrugations.

Ring-shank nails are used to attach the absorber to the baffles and edges. They're nailed into the valleys of every other corrugation after you've applied the sealing material.

Now for glazing. The method depends upon the material used. The Energy Project has favored the use of fiber reinforced/plastic

(FRP) glazing for ease of handling and low cost. FRPs may not come in first when it comes to looks, but they certainly are durable, and they allow for swift installation. Paul Phelps found out about the impact strength of FRP glazing when he accidentally gave it a full-force hammer swing. The strongest reaction to the impact was Paul's own gasp. The glazing merely dimpled slightly. Such resistance to breakage is important in a high traffic area like the Phelps' porch, where tempered glass wouldn't go unbroken for long.

The thin FRP material can be drilled and screwed on over 1 x 2-inch wooden spacers that have been attached around the perimeter (again with caulking and foam strips) and right over the location of the baffle. In collector systems with several baffles, such as the Stark's, glazing spacers must be placed frequently enough to support the glazing against buckling or rippling. After the spacers are attached they receive a bead of silicone wherever an edge of the glazing material will lay. Then it is unrolled and tacked down in one direction only, to ensure that it lays flat with no built-in ripples. Finally an exterior batten (¼-inch wood strips, or bronze anodized aluminum flat stock) is secured at every edge and seam (FRP edges are butted together, not overlapped) by drilling through the FRP into the spacers and screwing or nailing down. (Nailing through undrilled material can cause local fracturing.)

At attachment points that aren't battened, use screw or nail fasteners with neoprene washers, such as standard gasketed roofing nails.

To finish the perimeter it's good practice to add ¾-inch-thick wood boards that are ripped (cut lengthwise) to a width equal to the collector depth. If a top edge is exposed to weather, flashing is essential to prevent leaks into the collector. Another perimeter finishing option is to use L-shaped wood or metal corner trim to positively seal out the elements.

Rules of Thumb for Solar Air Collectors

Getting ready to build? The following guidelines have been developed by the Small Farm Energy Project and others working to optimize air-heating collectors. These calculations are designed to give prospective solarizers a much-better-than-ballpark set of numbers for sizing the collector area, air gap, fan, vent openings and, if used, storage.

1. To build a collector that operates without the need for storage, don't let the collector area exceed 20 percent of the house's heated floor area, if the house is reasonably well insulated.

2. Baffle layout should be such that no single "air run," the distance between an inlet and outlet, exceeds 32 feet. Larger collectors such as the Stark's are divided into two separate zones, though both are powered by a single fan. A multi-zone collector can also have outlets opening onto different parts of the house.

3. Fan-powered air flow should equal an "actual" two cfm per square foot of collector at sea level, and 3 cfm per square foot at an altitude of 7,000 feet, because of decreasing air density. ("Actual" flow is the fan's or blower's rated capacity (cfm) less the effects of resistance to air flow (called static pressure drop) caused by the friction of moving air against solid surfaces.) SFEP has calculated the average pressure drop through these collectors to be from .3 to .5 inch on an instrument that measures pressure change in "inches of water" in a column. (It gets complicated; just take us at our word.) Most fan and blower cfm ratings are given for a range of pressure drops, so choosing the right units won't be difficult. SFEP recommends direct drive blowers for small collectors (less than 150 square feet) and belt drive units (squirrel cage) for larger systems to allow for experimentation and fine-tuning with different pulley sizes. The goal for both of these is to produce the minimum temperature rise through the collectors—usually at least 20°F—while still maintaining an outlet air flow that gives off enough warmth. The cooler-running collector is more efficient because it transfers that much more heat to the house (and less back out through the glazing).

4. The air gap is a function of the air flow (volume over time) and the air velocity (speed over time). The optimal air flow is 800 feet per minute (fpm). Divide the calculated cfm by 800 fpm to get the area (in square feet) of the air gap cross section. The gap is then found simply by dividing the cross section area by the width of the collector airway in one direction of air flow.

In the Phelps' straight-through collector the total width is 45 inches and the designed air flow is 300 cfm. The area of the air gap is therefore 300 cfm/800 fpm = .375 square feet or 54 square inches. The air gap width is then found by: 54 sq. in./45-inch width = 1.2 inches. The Phelps settled on an air gap of 1¼ inches. The Stark's collector has a variable width of 11 to 16 feet due to the presence of windows. The average width was figured to be 13.5 feet but because the air flows through the collector in two directions, up and then down, the actual collector width in one direction is half the average width, or 6.25 feet (75 inches). At a design air flow of 550 cfm the calculation proceeds: 550 cfm/800 fpm = .6875 sq. ft. or 99 sq. in. Air gap width is: 99 sq. in./75-inch width = 1.32 inches. Again a 1¼-inch actual gap is close enough.

5. The collector inlets and outlets must be of a size equal in area to the airway (between baffles) they serve. For example, the Stark's airways were generally 16 inches wide with a 1.5-inch air gap. That means an area of 16 x 1.5 = 24 square inches. Thus, each vent opening was cut to measure 4 x 6 inches.

6. When duct work is needed to get a more extensive distribution of solar heat, the design velocity for ducting is 500 fpm. Thus, a 200-square-foot collector designed for a 500 cfm flow rate would need duct work with a cross-sectional area of 500 cfm/500 fpm or one square foot. A 12 x 12-inch duct could be used, or one 6 x 24 inches. It even is possible to build a duct onto an exposed basement ceiling using the floor joists and subfloor for three sides and thin plywood for the fourth side. Sealing air leaks with caulking and duct tape is crucial, along with providing duct insulation.

7. Storage. A rule of thumb on storage sizing calls for 50 to 60 pounds of rock per square foot of collector. Working with Btus, the specific heat of rock is such that one cubic foot stores 20 Btus for every 1°F it rises in temperature. In the case of a 40 degree F rise, a cubic foot would store 20 x 40 or 800 Btus. Let's say also that the collector output is 150,000 Btus per day. In order to store that much heat (at a 40 degree F design temperature rise): 150,000 Btu/day/800 Btu/cubic feet of rock = about 187.5 cubic

feet of rock needed, or about 18,750 pounds of the stuff. That's roughly seven cubic yards; one cubic yard weighing 2,700 pounds. The storage bin also should be proportioned for minimum surface area to minimize storage heat loss.

It should be stressed that incorporating storage into the collector system is no simple task, and because of space limitations we've by no means included all the information needed to do the work. Only the skilled craftsman who has some experience with forced-air heating systems should make the attempt.

A good source of information on these air collectors and storage systems is the Domestic Technology Institute. Their publications are available through Solstice Publications, Box 2043, Evergreen, CO 80439. Ask for publication #BP-044 "Solar Forced Air Heating System Plans," which is a set of six 18 x 24-inch blueprints available for $16.

Another source of plans for an air heating collector and rock storage system is the Ayer's Cliff Centre for Solar Research, Box 344, Ayer's Cliff, Quebec, Canada JOB 1 CO.

Adding the Juice

That's the collector. Now it has to be powered, and as the wiring diagram shows, there's not much to it. Power is brought through a manual switch (used for seasonal control) to the blower and the thermostatic control. Using the right blower is again a matter of a little calculation, depending primarily on the collector area (see guidelines). There are a few options for controls. A $35 remote bulb thermostat (Honeywell T675A or equivalent) allows for the sensing bulb to be located a short distance from the main box, usually bonded or mechanically affixed to the absorber plate near the collector outlet. This unit's "blower on" threshold or temperature setting can also be adjusted for fine-tuning the system.

Five dollars, on the other hand, gets you a simple "snap-disk" control, which is simply a switch controlled by temperature. It also is mounted at the outlet, but is not adjustable. Instead, it is available in preset switching temperatures; a 100 to 120 degrees F switch-on is desirable for these collectors.

The cheapest control is total manual switching, which, if it suits you, can become a quick, twice-a-day routine. Inconvenience may mount, however, if both you and the sun are gone for part of the day, leaving a blowing collector cool off the house.

Another important control to have is spring-louvered vents or manually closable registers at the collector inlet or outlet, whichever is the lower of the two. At night during cold weather cold air will want to "drop" out of the collector into the house, possibly drawing warm room air in the collector to replace it. Without vent control, such "re-verse thermosiphoning" can steal back much of the day's collected heat. Instead of losing heat outdoors, the Phelps rely on vent control.

Controlling the Heat

Because maximum control over the collected solar heat is the name of the game, it's downright obligatory to have insulation in place behind the collector. If not, some of the heat radiating from the back of the absorber plate simply migrates through the wall into the room. That may not be so bad during cold weather; all that's being sacrificed is an element of control and therefore some efficiency. During the warm months, however, the collector can heat up if it's not shaded, and without some thermal resistance (insulation) between it and the room there will be some unwanted interior heat gain. It's been assumed here that the building's stud wall has already been insulated (you're not adding solar to an uninsulated house, are you? Tsk, tsk), but if for some strange and unusual reason the collector wall isn't insulated, it should be added either to the stud wall cavity or placed behind the collector when it's built. No insulation should be left exposed directly to the absorber plate.

Getting back to warm weather "nonoperation" of the collector, it's likely that a large collector wall can't be totally shaded and thus will heat up from diffuse and reflected sunlight. Vents should be provided at the top and bottom of the collector to promote a cooling convective air flow that will exhaust heat to the atmosphere. For bottom vents, SFEP simply drilled a series of holes through the base of the collector, where they can be plugged with lag bolts or corks during the heating season.

The design of top vents depends on the collector design: whether or not a hinged vent can be operated from a second story window or reached by ladder to be operated seasonally. The Stark's collector also had the important feature of having been built around the windows so it doesn't impede the house's normal interior.

The Stark System

The basic collector and system design can, of course, be adapted to a variety of wall shapes and sizes; that's what makes it ideal for retrofitting onto frame houses. Generally, as collector area increases, the routing of air through it becomes somewhat more involved. Witness the configuration of Ken and Jan Stark's collector. The size and layout of this system was again primarily dictated by the available wall space, in this case making for a 16 x 17-foot collector (220 square feet). Because of the unit's size and the windows it had to be built around, and the fact that the inlet (receiving basement air) and outlet (into the first-floor living room) are placed at the bottom of the collector, the air flow could not be designed for a straight run. It had to be

"shaped" to force air through the entire collector to prevent wasteful dead-air hot spots. And to guard further against dead-air pockets, any baffle that butted perpendicularly into another baffle would be drilled to "leak" an air flow through a potentially dead corner. As the illustration shows, the baffling resembles a maze, but a closer look at the air flow indicators shows there's clearly a method to this maze. It also shows that the inlet and outlet ports are equal in number (six each) and area. This is essential to maintain a balanced air flow through both sides of the collector.

The lap siding on the Stark's house presented a problem of sealing the perimeter air gap spacer. The problem was solved by building the collector all the way out to the flat vertical corner trim. Had they not done that they could have used trusty foam strips to make a seal, or, if the siding were backed by solid plywood sheathing, they could have cut a 1¼-inch-wide groove in the siding to receive the 2 x 2-inch spacer flat to the plywood. Then caulking would have sufficed to make the final air seal. The second problem raised by the lap siding was excessive resistance to air flow. Discarded aluminum press plates provided the smooth solution: they were tacked to the wall inside the collector perimeter, and all was well.

Relative to the size of their house—about 900 square feet of heated floor area—the Stark's collector is a large one. The combination of a tight, insulated building and large collector area could lead to daytime overheating, in which excess heat would have to be "dumped" outside—wasted, in other words. There is, however, a rule of thumb concerning the collector-floor area ratio that can help prevent oversizing and heat dumping: if the collector area exceeds 15 to 20 percent of a building's floor area, a heat storage component should be included in the system. The common storage medium for hot air systems is small (.75 to 1.75-inch diameter) stones stored in an insulated bin and connected to the collector and existing furnace duct work. That kind of addition does indeed increase the complexity of the system, but not beyond the reach of the skilled craftsman.

As the illustration shows, the addition of thermal storage brings with it additional thermostatic and air flow controls, all of them automatic. These controls allow for more than the single on-off operating mode of the direct-heating, storageless system. If the house thermostat calls for heat during a sunny day, hot air will bypass the rock bin and enter the house directly from the collector. When the house is sufficiently heated, collector hot air is diverted through the spaces between the stones and pebbles, heating them up. Thus the rock bin becomes "charged" with heat and available for service in the third operating mode: house calls for heat; no heat is available from the collector (nighttime or a

heavily overcast day); so the automatic dampers and storage blower actuate to draw heat from the rock storage and distribute it through the house heating ducts. It may appear fancy, but it's not exotic. Every bit of hardware comes right off the shelf.

Now, anyone who's taking a serious look at solar heating is obviously looking for heat at a lower cost than that provided by their existing system. The solar wall collector comes out looking pretty good on that score. The Stark's collector had a materials' cost of about $575 or $2.60 per square foot, and the rock storage with the additional controls and duct work was estimated to cost again as much as the collector, bringing the total cost to about $5.25 per square foot collector area, which in the realm of solar heating systems rates the title "low cost." But low cost for what benefit? Ken Stark notes this: "Before we put up the collector we added insulation around the house, and cut the propane bill in half. The solar heat has cut it again by 35 to 40 percent." The SFEP calculates about the same by comparing the home's heat loss of 400,000 Btus (through an average January day at 15° F average outside temperature) with the collector's average clear day heat gain (for the same period) of 175,000 Btus (at 50 percent efficiency for the total system). The solar contribution is calculated to be about 43 percent, with the balance made up by the furnace. At that rate of heat production the system is likely to pay for itself in eight to nine years if the cost of energy continues to be so upwardly mobile.

Of course, the more sunlight the house receives, the sooner the system's cost is recovered. Snow is an energy booster, too, when it's covering the ground in front of the collector and reflecting more sunlight onto the absorber. SFEP estimates that snow causes at least a 10 to 20 percent increase in energy received by the collector.

With no heat storage mechanism, the Phelps' system cost about $2.25 per square foot for 120 square feet of collector, with the help of some recycled materials. Dub that system "very low cost." Using all new materials pushes the cost up to the not-so-princely sum of $2.60 per square foot. To evaluate this system the people at SFEP looked at its an-nual heating potential and came up with the wide range of 5.2 to 10.7 million Btus per heating season (given the vagaries of available sunshine).

The Phelps are buying electricity at 3¢/kwh, below the national average of 5¢/kwh, but even with minimum solar gain they still are saving about $50 a year and paying the system off in about six years. At the current price of #2 fuel oil, annual savings in the $55 to $115 range are possible. With the addition of the 66-square-foot collector the Phelps can look forward to a 25 percent solar contribution to their cold weather comfort.

These are the kinds of numbers that make solar heating sense. For Nebraska farmers, they add up to a lot of valuable hot air.

INSULATE ON THE OUTSIDE

What's to be done with an old brick home?
Tim Michels has found an answer
that helps cut his gas bill by four-fifths.

What do you do with a 43-year-old fuel-guzzling brick house?

That's what Tim and Wanda Michels asked themselves. Their uninsulated brick duplex in suburban St. Louis had been built in 1937, and stood two stories high, adorned with leaky single-glazed windows. In the basement, a gas-fired boiler fit for a battleship's engine room sent 1,200 degrees F steam through a maze of uninsulated pipes to keep the house warm by brute thermal force.

When the Michels bought the house in the mid-1970s, they discovered that heating was their biggest problem. Fuel bills had soared past the $1,000-per-year mark, and showed no inclination to recede. The building's basic structure was sound, but the costs of keeping warm rapidly were becoming prohibitive. Tim and Wanda quickly found themselves the owners of a brick brontohome with an insatiable appetite for money.

Instead of selling or scrapping the still-useful building, the Michels began a series of simple but extensive conservation measures—weatherization, insulation, and solar retrofitting—designed to place their home on a par with many of today's most efficient buildings. The results are amazing: today, their masonry dinosaur has been transformed into an efficient, modern residence that uses fully 80 percent less heating fuel than before, and receives half its heat from the sun.

Far from being unsalvageable, the Michels learned that homes like theirs offer great promise for energy efficiency because of the enormous heat-storage capacity of masonry building materials.

If a layer of insulation is added to the exterior of a brick, stone or concrete home, the building's mass is effectively moved *inside* where it becomes thermal mass, soaking up and releasing heat as needed. In addition, south-facing masonry walls can be converted into vented or unvented Trombe walls and sunspaces. These retrofits mean that older masonry homes need not be relegated to history's scrap heap.

Weatherization and Insulation

Tim began his energy program by tracking down and plugging all the drafts and heat leaks he could find. Seams and cracks were carefully caulked, doors were weather-stripped, and leaky windows were replaced with insulating storm/ screen combinations. Tim hand-made simple plastic windows to fit the porch's unusual arched openings, and fitted a storm door at the top of the porch steps to create a draft-free airlock for the front entries of both halves of the duplex.

Once the house was tightly sealed, rigid insulation was attached to the west, north, and east walls by friction-fitting, two-inch-thick polyurethane boards held between Z-shaped

Air warmed in the greenhouse rises into the house through the twin thermal chimneys which bracket the enlarged second story window.

metal channels which had been fastened to the bricks (see diagrams). An inexpensive metal lath was screwed to the metal strips and then covered with a high-quality resin-hardened stucco. This jacked up the insulative value of the exterior walls from R-4 to R-18. What's more the exterior insulation encloses the brick walls within the home's thermal environment. Now, in order for the home's interior temperature to fall, tens of thousands of pounds of masonry must also cool off, a process that takes many hours. Because such enormous quantities of heat are stored in the brick walls, the temperature inside the

The Michel's two-story duplex before alteration: Steam heat, uninsulated masonry walls and $1,200 fuel bills.

Construction began in summer. Tim did as much as he could, but hired professionals for most of the scaffold work.

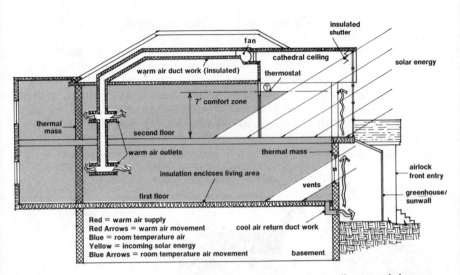

Air flow through the Michels' house is regulated by a mechanically assisted thermo-siphon. Air is warmed by incoming sunlight, and rises to the second floor's ceiling, where a small blower circulates the warmth throughout the house. As the air cools, it sinks and enters the greenhouse/sunwall area via floor ducts, where it can be reheated by the sun, to continue the cycle.

When finished, the house sported an enclosed airlock entry, full exterior insulation on three sides, and a south-facing sunwall with enlarged windows and a solar-heated-brick thermal mass.

Michels' home remains steady and comfortable.

"Just counting the innermost few inches of mass," Tim told me, "raising the temperature only 13 degrees puts over a million Btus into storage. That's enough for the house to coast without auxiliary heating for about two average St. Louis winter days or one bitterly cold day."

Tim credits this excellent performance to the care with which the house was sealed and insulated. "The main thing is that before you do anything else, you've got to reduce your overall heating loads. At least 60 percent of my fuel savings comes from weatherization and insulation alone. Now that my home's total amount of heating has been reduced, half the *remaining* load will be provided by solar input, for a total savings of 80 percent. It's only after you reduced the overall loads does solar heating become practical."

Tim's solar heating system is elegantly simple. Rather than insulate the home's south wall, he enlarged a bay window that had been part of the original facade to let the sun pour into the second story. He also double-glazed the window.This provides direct heating of the home's interior on clear winter days.

Tim then built a simple plastic-glazed, lean-to greenhouse over the first story south wall, and connected it to two glazed "thermal chimneys" on either side of the newly enlarged second story window (see photos). Vents were cut through the wall at the tops of the twin chimneys, and a floor-level duct installed at the base of the greenhouse. The plastic glazing traps solar energy, so that the masonry becomes quite warm after several hours of exposure to sunlight. Some of this absorbed heat is radiated into the home, while still more is given up to the air trapped beneath the glazing. Whenever the sun shines, a gentle, low speed convective loop is formed: air within the greenhouse becomes warm, rises through the thermal chimneys and through the vents into the second story, while cool air automatically enters the greenhouse through the floor-level ducts, where it is heated, rises, and so on, to continue the cycle. This steady supply of warm air provides indirect heating throughout much of the house. Combined, the direct and indirect solar heat keep indoor temperatures comfortable, and hold fuel-use to a minimum.

"I used a greenhouse glazing plastic called 'Flexigard 7410' on my south walls," Tim said. "I experimented with Lascolite and Mylar at first. The Lascolite was cloudy, which hid the exterior of the house and did nothing for the aesthetics of the neighborhood. It would be fine for rooftop collectors, but it's the wrong product for an application like mine. The Mylar worked well, but it was a little too thin for comfort. Flexigard (a 3M product) is guaranteed for ten years. It's also easy to work with, because you can cut it with scissors or tin snips, and

"I made these alterations because they made energy sense," said Tim. "But you know, I think the aesthetics alone would have warranted it."

just staple it in place."

Tim designed his greenhouse with hinge pins and wing nuts so it can be completely disassembled in summer. "Taking the greenhouse down was the simplest solution," he explained. "If I left it up all year, I'd have to install vents or shading devices to prevent summer overheating. Also, I'd lose summer ventilation from the first floor windows, which open directly into the greenhouse. Instead, I take the whole thing down in the spring, and simply avoid all the warm weather hassles." The greenhouse breaks down into several panels, glazing intact, which can be stored conveniently in a shed or garage over the summer months. This clever knock-down assembly means that the whole unit can be removed or replaced in only a few hours, helping keep long-term maintenance to a bare minimum.

Inside the house, Tim painted the walls white to allow the sunlight coming through the enlarged windows to diffuse through all the rooms. In winter, the low winter sun penetrates a full 32 feet into the Michels' home, warming the floors and reducing the need for artificial lighting. Even on gray days, the house is never gloomy.

"The house is so bright, so alive," Tim said, "I really like it. I went through a long time feeling the pressure to get it done, but now I can sit back and really begin to appreciate how these alterations have changed my feelings about living in a house.

You see, I grew up in the suburbs where a house was just a house. I ended up believing that if you wanted beauty, you went outside or took a vacation. But here, I don't have to go outdoors to enjoy the sunshine or a feeling of openness, because it's right here in my living room."

Tim's enthusiasm for his solar modifications isn't limited to aesthetics. "The winter before I started these alterations, I was posting gas bills of $180 to $200 a month during the coldest part of the winter, and gas here is relatively cheap. Last year, if I hadn't made any changes, I'd have spent at least $1,200 for heating. Instead, even with the solar option only 25 percent complete, I spent only $700, for a savings of 40 percent. Next winter, with everything finished, I'm looking forward to a $300 gas bill for the whole heating season." With savings like these, Tim will have cut his wintertime heating costs from around 50¢ per square foot of floor plan to just over 13¢ per square foot. Not bad for a 43-year-old home.

The energy savings add up quickly. "The payback time for the insulation and the sunwall should be under nine years," Tim said, "and that's pretty good. The improvements cost about $5 per square foot of floor plan, but also raised the property value by at least as much. I could sell the house right now and not lose a penny, and if I stay here for more than nine years, I'll be home free."

The home's blend of cost-cutting efficiency and good looks has drawn considerable attention, and Tim is justifiably proud of his accomplishment. "People stop when they're driving by to tell me how good it looks," he said, "and the neighbors think it's great that someone's finally trying to find an attractive way to make these old homes more efficient. A few have even gone so far as to talk with contractors about having the same things done to their homes. It's nice, when you're trying to promote solar, to have a house that gets this kind of favorable attention.

"In fact, if I'd had the vision as a designer to change my house this way, I would have done it just for the aesthetics, without any pressure from energy at all. But these changes are also energy efficient, so I have a sort of two-

Construction Detail

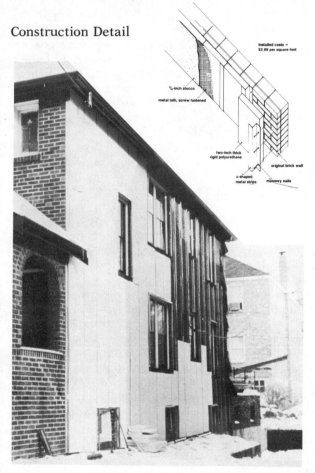

Construction proceeding on home's east wall.

The exterior insulation was applied in steps. (1) Z-shaped metal channels were fastened to the walls' mortar with masonry nails. (2) Rigid polyurethane boards, each two inches thick, were friction-fitted between the vertical metal strips. (3) Lightweight metal lath was screwed to the metal strips over the insulation. (4) The lath was filled and covered with a three-quarter-inch-thick layer of stucco. (5) Wooden trim-pieces were fitted around windows and doors to extend their frames out to the full depth of the new exterior surfaces of the wall. (6) All trim-pieces and seams were fully caulked with a high-quality silicone putty.

for-one home. No one should have to compromise beauty for efficiency and sit in a warm house that's nothing more than a warm dark box."

Tim's experience has convinced him of the value of retrofits, so he has plans for almost every other part of his house. He's already replaced the old boiler with a much smaller electrically ignited unit, and he's busy installing insulating curtains on all the home's windows. Once that's done, he wants to mount a small blower at the peak of the second floor's cathedral ceiling to help distribute the solar heat captured by the glazed south wall.

Because the house has been in constant use for more than 40 years, there's also plumbing and electrical work that needs attention. Tim views this as an opportunity: as each of the home's systems comes due for an overhaul, he'll do whatever he can to make it more efficient. In time, all the wiring will be upgraded, all the steam and hot water lines will be insulated, and even the small decorative stained glass windows in the living room will be carefully fitted with clear storm windows.

"It's great to be a designer of my own space," Tim said, "and to take direct hold of my environment. I'll let the lab boys do the hard research: I want to know what can be done in the real world, not in test cells. After all, I'm looking at a nine-year payback, so I have to ask myself as a homeowner, 'Is it really worthwhile?'

"I think it is, for me and for others in homes like this one. Both for financial reasons, and for the intangibles too, such as the improved aesthetics and the fresh tomatoes I expect to harvest from the greenhouse all winter long. These intangibles simultaneously increase the value and shorten the payback time, which helps encourage people to undertake a project of this size. Then, when you factor all these elements into the question 'Should this be done?', the only possible answer is 'Yes'."

THE TROUBLE WITH WINDOWS

(And What To Do)

If you're wondering where you should insulate your house, step over to one of your windows tonight, untuck your shirt, and press a pound of flesh against the glass. Not only will you quickly tuck in again, but you'll realize what else has to be covered up in order to cut your heating bills.

Windows are nice. They let the sun shine in, allow you to see what the neighbors are up to, and give the kids something to aim at when they're playing baseball. But windows are also burglars. At night, when you're not looking, they steal your heat. A typical home can lose 25 to 30 percent of its heat through windows. If it's a house with a lot of large windows, the figure can climb to 50 percent or higher.

The culprit, of course, is the glass itself. It's a lousy insulator. If you doubt it, here's another experiment you can perform. Make yourself a pot of coffee and pour some of the hot liquid into an ordinary drinking glass. In a minute or so, the outside of the glass will have become so hot you won't be able to pick it up. So much for the insulating ability of glass. Now

Window Quilt *is a thermal shade of five layers of fabric, reflective plastic, and polyester fibers. It's made by Appropriate Technology Corp.*

pour some more of the coffee into a white polystyrene cup. You can nurse the drink for as long as you want and the container won't be warm to the touch, because the foam is an effective insulator.

A single-glazed window,

which has an R-value of less than one, can conduct as much as 20 times more heat from your house than an insulated wall of the same size. Double-glazed "insulating glass" can halve that amount, but there's still a lot of heat going out the window.

Most of you have already insulated your attics to R-30 or better. You've insulated your exterior walls to at least R-11. But your windows, at R-1 or R-2, are hanging out like a madman in a T-shirt on a snowy day. It's easy to understand. Insulating your windows isn't an obvious thing. You can't go to the local hardware store and buy a set of thermal shutters. There aren't any big national advertising campaigns telling you to tighten up your windows. Maybe that's because window insulation is not a simple product to be hidden away in your walls. It's right out in the open, subject to personal decorating taste, and its construction depends upon the infinite variety of window shapes and sizes. In that way, window insulation is a task well suited to the do-it-yourselfer. So if you've already insulated in other ways, insulating your windows is probably the first project you should undertake this fall.

Just why is it that windows lose so much heat? One reason is air infiltration around the glass. It can add greatly to your total heating bill. Caulking and weather-stripping go a long way toward stopping infiltration, and window insulation goes one step further.

The Insul Shutter, *Manufactured by a Colorado firm, is a window insulation that comes in a kit.*

Even if you seal up all the leaks *around* the glass, you're still losing a lot of heat *through* it. Heat is constantly in motion. Seeking to equalize itself, heat moves from hot to cold. The transfer takes place in three different ways: conduction, convection and radiation.

Conduction is the way that heat travels through a material; in this case, glass. It's the reason a drinking glass of coffee gets too hot to handle. Different materials conduct heat in different ways.

Aluminum and glass conduct heat very well. Insulation offers much more resistance to heat transfer.

Convection is the transfer of heat by air movement. Warm air is lighter and rises, while heavier cold air sinks. Enter your cold window. Warm room air against the window is cooled by conduction and falls to the floor, making room for more warm air to come in contact with the glass. A current is created. Putting something between the air and the cold glass—a layer of insulation or another pane of glass with an air pocket between the two—breaks the current.

To put it more simply than it probably should be, *radiation* is the way heat is transferred from object to object through space. In other words, it's not only the temperature of the air in a room, but the temperature of the objects around you that make you feel comfortable. Everything gives off radiant energy, but warmer objects give off more than colder ones. Heat moves from warmer things to colder things. Enter, once again, your cold window. The colder it is, the more heat it sucks from your body if you're near it, and the more uncomfortable you feel, even if the thermostat says you should be toasty.

So much for the physics. Now let's talk, in practical terms, about your windows and what you can do. There are two basic choices: add more glazing (either glass or plastic), or add a piece of portable wall that covers the glass . . . movable insulation, it's called. You can add one or the other, or both.

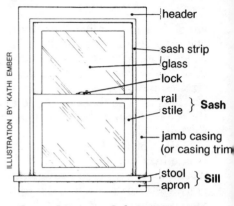

ILLUSTRATION BY KATHI EMBER

header
sash strip
glass
lock
rail } Sash
stile
jamb casing (or casing trim
stool } Sill
apron

Anatomy Of A Window

The stories that follow go into detail about the possible variations you can try—more glass or movable insulation. Briefly, here's what you can do.

No matter which side of the house the window is located on, double glazing outperforms single glazing. When you add an extra layer of glass, you're creating an air pocket between the panes that inhibits conduction of heat to the outside. Storm windows are the easiest, although not the cheapest, way to add extra glazing. If you already have storm windows, by all means use them. In general, ones with wooden sashes work better than those with aluminum, because wood doesn't conduct heat as easily. Triple-track "combination" storm windows usually offer only minimal insulation because their relatively loose seals allow air infiltration.

Most new storm windows are made of aluminum, and they aren't cheap—about $4 per square foot. Storms eventually pay for themselves in 5–10 years.

You may also be able to add a permanent sheet of glass to your existing window casement. If you're planning to replace your windows entirely, you can buy prefabricated double-glazed windows. These may be simply two separate sheets of glass held together by a weatherproof frame, or two panes fused together. In either case, the seal has to be good, or moisture can build up between the panes, causing condensation and spoiling your view. Permanent double glazing usually is preferable over storm windows for several reasons. The seal around storms is seldom airtight, so some cold air seeps in. Also, there's no time-consuming seasonal mounting and removal.

All this talk about extra glass raises a question: If two panes are better than one, aren't three better than two? Maybe. Triple glazing can cut heat loss to two-thirds the loss from a double-glazed window. But it also cuts light transmission by 10 percent. The latter is an important point for south-facing windows, which work for you on a winter's day, letting in heat and light. On north-, east-, and west-facing windows, where solar heat gain is not a significant consideration, triple glazing performs much better.

Getting that third layer of glazing doesn't come ▾cheaply. Chances are you won't be able to add it yourself to existing windows, so you'll have to buy new, triple-glazed units, which cost about $50–$60 more per window than double glazing. Unless you're building a new house or doing some serious remodeling, triple glazing may not be worth the investment. If you are building, or replacing, you may want to dispense with the third layer of glass on south-facing windows, especially if you have cold, but sunny, winters.

There is a cheaper way than glass. You can add an extra layer of rigid plastic or plastic film to your existing windows. The plastic is usually placed on the inside of the window. The cheapest of the cheap glazings is polyethylene which costs less than a nickel per square foot. A slightly more expensive option is clear plastic film, and the top of the line is rigid plastic. It can be cut to size with a jigsaw or band saw and taped or screwed to your window sash. Plastic frame kits are also available. Although it looks like glass, rigid plastic scratches much more easily and requires some care in handling.

Adding extra glazing has certain built-in-limitations. At best, you'll only be able to boost a window's R-value to three. More than three layers of glass makes your house noticeably dim inside. If you've set a goal greater than R-3 for your windows, movable insulation is your solution. During the day, you get the full benefit of the glass. At night, when there's not much to see anyway, you can block up the window and stop it from giving away your heat. Movable insulation comes in a variety of forms and materials. You can buy it in kit form, purchase plans, or build it from scratch.

Pop-in shutters, pieces of rigid insulation that are pressed over your windows at night, are a sim-

If you don't want to buy window insulation, you can make it yourself. These homemade bifold shutters on a New Jersey home were made of 3/4-inch flakeboard four years ago, and they're still as good as new, reports the owner, Tilly Spetgang.

Beadwall is a Spectacular way to go if you want to include insulated windows in new construction. Here you see the space within the windows being filled with insulating beads. Beadwall is made by Zomeworks.

ple, relatively inexpensive form of movable insulation. Kits are available, or you can make your own. Whether you're building or buying, a shutter should be constructed of a lightweight insulation such as rigid foam board. Anything heavier is difficult to move around and even more of a pain to keep in place.

Which brings us to one of the drawbacks of pop-in shutters: You've got to pop them out each morning, pop them in every night, and find someplace to store them in between. If you have the room, you can opt for hinged or sliding shutters. If you're building or remodeling, consider sliding shutters that slip away out of sight behind walls when you don't want them.

Still another way to tuck in your house for the night is with a thermal shade. It operates like an ordinary window shade—you pull it down when you need it and roll it back up when you don't. But

unlike your thin vinyl shades, which do little to cut heat losses, thermal shades can reduce heat loss through single-glazed windows by 50 percent or more.

Like shutters, thermal shades can be made from a variety of materials. Many people use quilted fiber fill about ½-inch thick. Thinness is important in insulating shades, because they can get quite bulky when they're rolled up. Shades often incorporate layers of reflective foil separated by airspaces. The shiny material cuts down radiant heat loss by reflecting heat back into the room.

Thermal curtains have gotten a bit of a bum rap, mainly because of false claims made by manufacturers whose products have little or no insulating value. Most of the decorative curtains and drapes on the market aren't designed to stop heat from escaping. They hang loose, away from windows, and let air pass both through and around them. In order to have any value as an insulator, a true thermal curtain must seal at the bottom and sides so air won't convect around it. The material should resist air flow through it and, preferably, have airspaces or fiber fill for insulation. Like shades, some thermal curtains have foil or silvered backings to reflect radiant heat.

As you see, there are lots of things you can make or buy that will tighten up your windows. But you want to know what works best. In his book *Movable Insulation*, William Langdon provides an answer. He did computer sim-

Windows In A Northern Climate: How The Options Perform

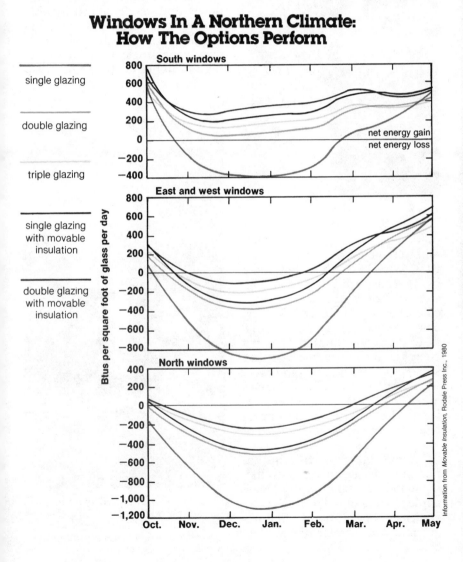

Information from *Movable Insulation*, Rodale Press Inc., 1980

77

Among other things, the chart should help you see which windows need your attention first. If you plan to tighten up your windows a few at a time, those facing north call out for immediate attention, followed by those facing east and west.

If you have single-pane windows and can't afford double glazing *and* insulation, or triple glazing, then movable insulation over your single-glazed window does seem like the next best thing.

This pop-in thermal shutter is something you can easily make yourself.

ulations of south-, east-, north- and west-facing windows in Madison, Wisconsin, that show double glazing with R-5 movable insulation to be the winner in a cold climate. The accompanying chart shows the double glazing/insulation combination is a net energy gainer through the entire season on south, east and west windows. North-facing windows are incorrigible losers of energy, but the losses with double glazing and insulation were smallest of all the options.

Single glazing with insulation finished second on south-facing windows, but dipped below triple glazing on all others. In every case, single-glazed windows put in a poor showing as net losers.

The Thermo Shade *is made of interlocking extruded plastic slats. It rolls in and out of the valance at top. Its maker claims "an effective R-5" insulation value when placed over a single-glazed window.*

But expect a slight problem. When insulation is placed over cold, single-glazed windows, the room air that's trapped between the two can condense and leave a film of moisture on the window. The condensation makes it difficult to see through the window when the insulation is removed, and you may have to mop little puddles off your sills and sashes some mornings. Condensation should be much less of a problem if double glazing is used with insulation.

When considering what to do about your windows, you also have to be honest with yourself. Will you be religious about closing the shades and shutters every night, or will you let it go when you're too tired? The saying that "passive homes require active owners" is especially true when it comes to movable insulation. The insulation isn't going to do you a whole lot of good if it's buried under a pile of the kid's toys when it should be up on the window. Double and triple glazing, on the other hand, are always on the job at night, whether or not you think about them.

There are lots of alternatives to throwing your heating dollars out the window. Some are cheap, others are not so inexpensive. Some are complex, others incredibly simple. In short, there's an answer to everyone's window problem.

For further reading:
Movable Insulation, William K. Langdon, Rodale Press, Emmaus, PA, 1980
Thermal Shutters and Shades, William A. Shurcliff, Brick House Publishing Co., Andover, MA, 1980
Weatherproofing, by the editors of Time-Life Books, Time-Life Books, Alexandria, VA, 1977

The windowBlanket *is a blend of traditional drape and modern window insulation. Its sides can be attached to the window frame for a side seal, and the added valance is a good idea to keep warm room air from getting in contact with the cold glass.*

PASSIVE SOLAR:
A NEW WAY
TO HEAT HOMES

Ever since the 1973 oil embargo, solar energy has been a favorite topic. Unfortunately, the impression has often been that solar power would be accomplished by a technological gadget sitting on or alongside the house which magically converted the sun's energy into whatever energy form was needed. Practical considerations of physics, economics and aesthetics were ignored as one pet scheme after another was promoted. As a result, solar energy came to be portrayed as "20 years away."

Fortunately a more realistic approach to solar energy is now being taken. Two solar technologies have emerged as being of

This design by Wayne Nichols combines direct gain with a Trombe wall. The wall is constructed of thin concrete with hollowed sections into which water-filled plastic bags are housed. The exterior fold-up door (shown fully opened in picture) is made of a reflective insulator and serves a dual purpose: it increases available light into the house during the day and prevents nighttime heat loss.

paramount practical importance. These are solar water heating and passive solar space heating. This article deals specifically with passive solar home heating.

What should we ask of a new shelter? (A new shelter might be built from scratch or it might be a modification of an old shelter.) We should ask for protection from the elements, an adequate level of comfort and a pleasurable environment that enhances our life. These features should be supplied economically, simply, reliably. Shelter should not dominate our lives but rather make minimum impact upon us. Ideal-

ly, a shelter should make us aware of the beauties and delights of nature rather than remove us from them.

The modern trend in shelter has failed us. We have practiced technological overkill devising wondrous and magnificent machines which convert fuel to heat and pump it to and fro in an attempt to impress our will over natural processes. It has led us to a dead end.

Passive solar is a new direction. It is not just a different technological solution to the house heating problem but an attempt to live with nature rather than

Figure 1. *A direct gain approach to passive solar heating is the simplest and most frequently employed. Winter sunshine entering through south-facing glazing is absorbed within the living space of the building and stored in mass within the building. If the daytime solar gains are greater than the energy requirement during the day, then heat storage is essential in order to retain the energy throughout the night. If that's not done, the house gets too warm by day and too cold by night. The masonry floor is effective heat storage only if it is directly sunlit. Walls are used for heat storage and are frequently insulated on the outside.*

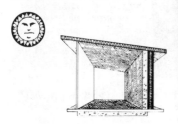

Fig. 1

81

overpowering it. The satisfying fact is that this not only is possible but relatively easy.

What Is Passive Solar?

A passive solar system is one in which heat moves by natural means. That is, the transport of heat from one place to another is by natural processes of convection, conduction and radiation. These processes are present in every structure, but the passive solar approach relies entirely on them and not on the use of pumps, fans or outside energy. Active solar systems, on the other hand, use a separate solar collector to heat either a liquid or air, and a pump or fan to move the heat to a separate thermal storage.

Some designs are primarily passive but do contain some active element, generally a fan, to assist in the distribution of heat. These are called "hybrid" designs. Even here the desire is to

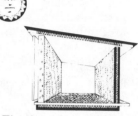

Fig. 2

Figure 2. *The thermal storage wall uses a mass wall located immediately behind the south glazing. This mass wall prevents the sun from entering the living space and thereby reduces three of the disadvantages of the direct gain approach: glare, fading of fabrics due to ultraviolet rays and large temperature swings from day to night. The thermal storage wall can be made of any heat-conductive storage material but generally, either masonry or contained water is used. A masonry wall is often called a Trombe wall after its French inventor Felix Trombe.*

This New Mexico home is part of a new solar development designed by Wayne Nichols. The Trombe wall contains interior windows that replace warm and cold air vents. This design is especially suitable for solar retrofits on existing homes.

minimize the dependence on the active element, relying on it primarily for enhanced performance rather than as a necessary element of the system.

There are five common passive solar design approaches. These are shown schematically in the following diagrams.

Aiming South

The primary "solar collector" in a passive solar building is frequently glass or other glazing material such as plastic or fiberglass sheet. By placing the glass so that it faces within 20 degrees of true south a maximum of energy is obtained in the winter and a minimum in the summer. East- or west-facing windows have just the opposite characteristic: maximizing summer heating and minimizing the winter solar gains. This strong preference for a south-facing window results from the path of the sun across the sky. In the winter the sun is generally low in the sky and toward the

Fig. 3

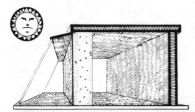

Figure 3. *The sunspace is a mixture of the direct gain and thermal storage wall designs and is sometimes referred to as an attached solar greenhouse. The left-hand section is a direct gain room with extensive glazing and is a very appropriate space for raising plants. It might also be used as an entryway, atrium, conservatory or simply as a hall. The right-hand space is protected from the day/night temperature swings in the sunspace by the thermal storage wall between them.*

The residence of Mike and Judy Corbett uses direct gain through insulated skylights and south-facing windows. The daytime heat is absorbed both by floor tiles and water-filled columns that line the back wall.

south, rising in the southeast and setting in the southwest.

In the summer, however, the sun rises in the northeast, swings nearly overhead at noon and sets towards the northwest. Thus the south face of the building receives very little sun in the summer but the east and west sides and roof receive a maximum amount. Correct passive design takes advantage of this natural situation by constructing the east and west sides of the building with a minimum of glazing that is well protected by shading.

The north side of the building presents a completely different problem. Here the strategy is to provide protection from the weather by use of generous insulation and protection from the wind which frequently blows from the north in the winter. In

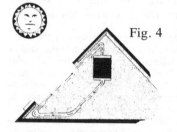

Fig. 4

Figure 4. *The convective loop approach is most akin to the normal active system because there is a separate solar collector and a separate heat storage connected by piping or ducting. Because the collector is located below the storage, the heated fluid rises by natural convection, deposits its heat in the heat storage and returns by natural convection to the collector. (Water heaters have been built according to this principle for years.) Space heating systems that use air as the heat transfer fluid also incorporate this principle.*

This home also combines active and passive solar. Copper flat-plate collectors supply both hot water and the majority of heat. The heated water is pumped from the collectors both to a storage tank and through plastic pipes set in the concrete slab. Additional heat from the south-facing glass is stored in the tile flooring. Home of John Watson, Davis, California.

many passive buildings the north side of the building is dug into the ground with the dirt piled up or "bermed" halfway or all the way up the north wall. Such a berm has the added advantage of deflecting north winds over the house.

Thermal Mass

Many days the sun provides more heat than is necessary to maintain comfort. Then after sundown the building temperature drops. Effective use of heavy materials, such as masonry floors and walls or barrels of water, can greatly reduce this problem. Some of the excess heat goes to warming up these materials which has the effect of storing the heat for later use. After sundown the building temperature will drop less rapidly as the floor and walls gradually cool down and give up their stored heat. Such heat storage materials are most effective when located directly in the sun.

With the thermal storage wall, maximum effectiveness is guaranteed by placing the heat storing material immediately behind the window. The masonry or "Trombe wall" approach has the particular advantage of greatly reducing the temperature swings on the inside, especially if the wall is at least 14 inches thick. The primary advantage of a water wall is its ability to obtain very large thermal storage, enough to store more than one day's heat, in a wall of reasonable dimension. A major problem here is figuring a way to contain the water permanently, attractively and economically. Various techniques now being employed are: freestanding plastic or metal tubes, rectangular fiberglass or metal boxes, jars, bottles and barrels.

Advantages of Passive

Lower costs. The extra cost incurred in order to incorporate passive solar depends on the design approach. In a typical case, adding 400 square feet of solar glazing might cost anywhere from $1,000 to $6,000. Direct gain tends to be the cheapest but can become expensive if large glazed areas are used; thus requiring additional massive heat storing walls within the living space. Trombe walls tend to be relatively more expensive and sunspaces less expensive, if one accounts for the value of the space obtained. Costs tend to be low for passive systems because materials are available and builders are familiar with your use. Of course, the slightly higher construction costs are offset by lower fuel bills. The typical payback period for passive details is four to ten years.

Ease of Operation. A well-designed passive home is easy to live in, requiring little work and participation on the part of the homeowner.

Reliability. Most passive systems are designed with conventional materials that have been well tested in service. There is no mechanical equipment to go wrong.

Comfort. Heating a house using large warm walls or floors is much more comfortable than by heating the air. This comfort is characteristic of passive solar

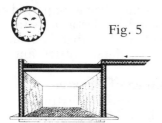

Fig. 5

Figure 5. *In the thermal storage roof, or roof pond, the storage mass (water) is located in the building's ceiling. A principal advantage to this approach is that it offers the opportunity for an effective cooling system as well as a heating system by using radiation to the night sky and evaporative cooling. Some kind of movable insulation is required in order for this concept to work. The insulation is placed over the roof pond at night in the winter and during the day in the summer. This approach works best in dry climates.*

This California home of Ian MacGregor and Susan Garbini incorporates a hybrid system. Heat is received through eight roof collector panels and stored in a 260-gallon water tank. The heated water is then pumped through copper coils set into the concrete floors. Direct gain passive solar aids the active by the use of south and clerestory windows.

86

buildings. Properly designed, they can be relatively stable in temperature without additional means of control. This is especially true of the Trombe wall and the living space behind an attached greenhouse.

Livability. Passive solar buildings are enjoyable spaces that enhance the life of the occupants. Because the building is generally more open to the environment and natural light, it provides a good space for growing plants and a heightened awareness of nature's delights and the weather.

Aesthetic Appeal. Although passive solar buildings sometimes look different from their more conventional neighbors, their appearance is generally considered appealing. Large expanses of glass, if properly done, can be an architectural asset. Many architectural features such as picture or clerestory windows and massive fireplace sections in a building can be turned to good thermal use by establishing the proper relationship of these elements to the building's geometry and orientation. Shading overhangs and shutters also can add to the building's architectural variety. Availability of sunlight within the living space opens the possibility of adding growing plants for the joy of their beauty, variety and ever-changing characteristics.

Good Performance. Passive solar buildings work surprisingly well throughout the entire range of climates in the United States, providing 50 to 90 percent of needed heat from the sun. This has been predicted by analysis and confirmed through the experience of many passive buildings in Oregon and Kentucky, Maine and California, Virginia and Iowa, as well as the sunny Southwest.

Designs for Existing Buildings

Although some think that passive design is only suitable for new construction, there are, in fact, several approaches which can be used for existing buildings.

1. Adding south-facing windows. This provides additional direct gain to a structure which already may have very adequate heat storage built in, especially if it's an older building.

2. Adding a sunspace. The sunspace, or attached solar greenhouse, is proving to be a very popular addition; as much for the added food growing potential, natural winter humidity and the ambience as for the extra heat.

3. Adding a convective-loop air heater outside an existing south-facing insulated wall. These air heaters are lightweight and inexpensive and are especially effective because they can be built to shut off at night by means of a simple passive backdraft damper. They're also suitable for apartments or other multistory structures.

4. Glazing an existing south-facing masonry wall. This can turn a liability into an asset. Typical uninsulated brick or cement block walls have thermal resistance values as low as R-3—nowhere near the R-19 insulative value now being recommended for new construction in northern climates. But when glazed to make a Trombe wall, it becomes a net energy gainer—far better than an insulated wall.

THE NO-FRILLS, NO-FURNACE HOUSE THAT GENE BUILT

Double walls, superinsulation, and $50 annual fuel bills

"Something's radically wrong with the gospel according to conventional home builders." Gene Leger was speaking about his favorite subject—energy-efficient housing—and as he warmed to the theme, his voice began to boom. "If you follow the advice most builders give, you either end up with a house only half as efficient as it could be, or an efficient house you can't afford."

Gene believes he's found a way to deliver the benefits of efficient construction without the high costs. Along with a handful of other builders and contractors around the country, Gene designs his homes with superinsulated double walls.

"I did a thorough analysis of different wall structures before we bought our first nail, in order to see what would work best," Gene recalls. "First, I looked at mass walls which have worked well in sunny climates, and are becoming popular throughout the nation. After all, massive homes are relatively easy to build: any concrete supplier can drive to your site and literally pour you a house with high mass and relatively low R in the walls, so that thermal energy can enter the house and 'charge' the mass with heat. But here in Massachusetts and in other cold, cloudy climates, the benefits of massive construction are outweighed by the high cost of masonry. You end up with an expensive house that can't ever be charged fully with solar heat because the sun simply doesn't shine enough.

Location:
Pepperell, Massachusetts
Living Area:
1,100 square feet
Selling Price:
$53,900
in January 1980
(includes building lot)
Heating System:
Baseboard hot water
Owner:
John Gallant
Builder:
Gene Leger (Vista Homes)

Only the thickness of the window sills tells you there's something different about Gene's home. "I designed this house to fit into the neighborhood," he said, "and not to jar anyone's sensibilities."

"Next, I looked at a combination of low mass with high R: superinsulation. Everyone knows that adding extra insulation can reduce the need for space heat-ing, but as it turns out, super-insulation makes space heating almost unnecessary. With super-insulation, you retain almost all the heat that's generated inside a home by lights, appliances and the people. If the R value of the home's exterior is high enough, outside sources of heat become almost insignificant, and you simply don't need much, if any, auxiliary heating.

"In fact, I'll go even further than that: any house that has to be fitted with solar collectors or huge amounts of south glass or that requires more than pocket change for heating fuel, simply wasn't designed properly in the first place."

Gene settled on superinsulated levels of R-43 in his home's walls, and R-40 in the ceiling, figuring that his 1,100-square-foot house would require about $30 per year in auxiliary heating.

"With costs like these, you can see why I avoided any elaborate solar collection scheme. At $30 per year, it would take a lifetime to pay back even a small solar heating system. Mind you, there's nothing wrong with solar, but my point is that a well-designed house simply won't need the sun, or any other major source of auxiliary heat."

Unlike solar homes, which require orientation to the sun and exacting calculations of glazing area, superinsulated homes warm themselves from the inside, so that the external environment simply doesn't matter much. Superinsulated homes can be built in virtually any climate, and in any size, shape, style or orientation. In fact, they're about the only type of high-efficiency home that works in areas forbidden by solar architecture, such as deeply shadowed forest sites or on cold north slopes. "Sure," Gene said, "it's nice to use the sun when it's available, so I put my home's largest windows (about 100 square feet of glass) on the south wall. But with superinsulation, space heating from *any* outside source is almost a trivial concern." (In fact, Gene now feels he has put *too much* glass on the south wall, because the house has occasionally overheated, and can be almost uncomfortably warm inside on sunny days.)

Once Gene decided on superinsulation, he then looked at a number of different ways of building the frame walls to hold the nine-inch thickness of insulation he was considering. To his surprise, thick frame walls had first been pioneered in the 1940s by the Small Homes Council of the University of Illinois, which was then looking for inexpensive ways to house America's returning war veterans. "Thick walls never really caught on," Gene said, "because of the wide-board lumber costs. To avoid this, I decided to use two separate lightweight walls made of two-by-fours set on 24-inch centers. Placed side-by-side, these two thin walls create one thick wall that can cost less than a wall of the same thickness made of single, wide studs; especially in very cold climates where insulation should be R-35 or greater." (In milder regions, the extra costs of double-wall construction may not be justified.)

As Gene discovered, super-

90

insulated double walls can out-perform single-studded walls in other areas, too. Double walls, for example, can be constructed to any desired thickness merely by repositioning the inner wall. "It provides you with much more on-site flexibility," Gene said. And regardless of the final thickness of the wall, framing and erection costs remain constant, although (naturally) a thicker wall requires more insulation.

There's another boost that comes with double walls. In con-

A tiny wall-hung Paloma-Pak boiler burns natural gas to supply all the home's hot water and auxiliary heating needs. (The boiler is the vacuum-cleaner-sized device beneath the galvanized flue pipe.) Extra heated water is stored in the adjacent insulated tank until needed.

ventionally studded walls the two-by-fours, sixes (or whatever you choose), run all the way from one side of the wall to the other. Because wooden studs have a lower R value than the insulation packed between them, the studs act as a path of conductive heat loss. Of course, no one's ever gone broke from the amount of heat escaping through any one stud but, in a home with hundreds of studs, the heat loss adds up to extra wintertime fuel use. Double walls sidestep this problem by isolating the inner from the outer studs with an unbroken layer of insulation. The inner and outer studs never touch, so the wall has no conductive heat path to bleed away a home's heat.

There are more subtle thermal effects, too. Double walls can easily be made extra thick to avoid "air intrusion." Unlike ordinary infiltration, which blows air past a thermal barrier, air intrusion is the motion of air through the outer layers of an insulating material, as when wind blows through a poorly sealed sheathing and partially permeates an insulating batt. Moving air carries away heat, so air intrusion reduces the useful R of insulation. Proper sealing of the sheathing prevents most air intrusion—but with double-wall construction, a builder can also allow for unexpected air intrusion (as from shoddy workmanship) simply by repositioning the inner wall to add a few extra inches of insulation. Then, if air intrusion occurs, it affects only the surplus insulation leaving the bulk of the thermal barrier to operate at its full-rated R value.

A house built with double walls also can be more *thoroughly* insulated than conventional homes. In standard construction, flooring headers (the horizontal boards that attach floor joists to a wall or sill) are usually a thermal weak point. But with double walls, the flooring header is protected from cold outdoor temperatures by a full layer of insulation: "Instead of building the floor on top of the foundation and then building the walls on the floor, you can build double walls from the sill to the soffit and then hang the floor inside the double wall wherever you want. This way, the entire outside wall is evenly insulated from the foundation all the way to the roofline," Gene explained.

Finally, because double walls are inherently strong, they're well suited for trussed roofs, which eliminate the need for interior load-bearing walls. Floor plans can be any shape or even completely open. Future remodeling costs will be much lower than with standard construction and all plumbing and electrical work is simplified. "The plumber commented that our prototype home was a delight to work in," Gene said, "because he didn't have to spend a lot of time—time I would have had to pay for—figuring out how to drill through, brace or avoid load-bearing members. I don't know the exact numbers, but it saved me quite a few dollars right there."

Fresh Air without Freezing

The average well-built new home undergoes roughly one air change per hour (ACH), which is a shorthand way of saying that all the home's heated or cooled air is leaked away every 60 minutes. The heating or cooling system constantly has to play catch-up, replacing the energy bled away to the outdoors.

But Gene Leger's house is not your average home. His special construction details make his house three to four times tighter than a conventional new home. The Saskatchewan Conservation House is five times tighter than the average new home. These houses save energy because they trap their heated air. Unfortunately, they also trap the air's unseen burden of pollution. The pollution comes from household activities and, in some cases, the house itself.

Recent studies undertaken at Lawrence Berkeley Laboratories (LBL) in California, have found that the air inside extremely tight homes can be startlingly bad. Levels of nitrogen dioxide in unventilated kitchens where gas ovens are in operation can reach 250 parts per billion (ppb), a level normally associated with downtown rush-hour air. The maximum safe limit for formaldehyde and other aldehydes is 100 ppb, but some supertight homes have aldehyde levels (given off by insulation, particle board, wood panels and the like) of 266 ppb.

Even more alarming are the

tests that LBL researchers conducted at four airtight homes which were built with massive construction materials. When they closed up the houses on a calm day to achieve the lowest possible infiltration rates, they found levels of radioactive radon gas—given off by water, natural gas and massive building materials like brick, stone and concrete—fully 30 times higher than in standardly built homes and 6.25 times higher than the level at which the federal government calls for "prompt remedial action" in public places.

Do you have to worry about this? Chances are, not at all. The troubles begin to show up only in houses that are so airtight, they have considerably less than half an air change per hour. Your house would have to be built like Gene Leger's to achieve that kind of ACH. Research indicates that an ACH of .25 to .5 is enough to maintain a healthy interior.

If you were living in a too-tight house, you'd probably know it. You'd say "yes" to these questions: does your home collect odors after it's been closed for several hours? Do you often have to step outside for "a breath of air"? Do guests complain of allergies when they visit or does your family suffer from more head colds than average?

A more objective "tightness test" is to observe the operation of your home's combustion appliances. If you can operate your furnace, water heater, fireplace or wood stove *without* having to crack open a window or use an independent vent to supply combustion air to each device, your home probably has enough infiltration to protect your family from interior pollution. If your fireplace or wood stove works better with a window open, or if your furnace or water heater is equipped with a fresh-air supply vent of its own, then your home is extremely tight.

Because extreme air-tightness results in indoor air pollution, some people have jumped to the conclusion that insulation is dangerous. Nonsense. What's needed, instead, is a device newly introduced into this country that allows for efficient ventilation without high heat losses: an air-to-air heat exchanger. Air-to-air heat exchangers come in a variety of shapes and sizes, but all operate in the same basic manner. One small fan or blower draws a stream of fresh air into the home, while a second fan or blower pushes the same amount of air out. The two air streams flow past each other, separated by a thin barrier of metal, plastic or specially treated paper. Although the two air streams never physically mix, *heat* from one stream passes through the barrier into the opposing stream so that the incoming air is either preheated or precooled (as needed) by the stale exhaust air. This way, the home receives a steady supply of fresh air, while wasting very little of the exhaust air's energy.

Residential air-to-air heat exchangers cost from $200 for a small window-hung unit to over

$2,500 for the largest whole-house units. The energy savings range from about $50 per year to over $300 per year, depending on local climate and fuel costs. The health benefits of fresh, pollution-free air cannot be assigned a dollar value, but they're probably even more significant.

Here are a few sources in the emerging marketplace of heat exchangers:

Do-It-Yourself

The Extension Division of the University of Saskatchewan offers free, fairly detailed plans for a do-it-yourself heat exchanger costing about $60 for the basic materials. Blowers, controls and ducts add perhaps another $75 to the final cost (each installation will vary). The base model, designed by University of Saskatchewan mechanical engineering professors Robert Dumont, Robert Besant, and Dick Van Ee,

handles about 100 cfm (cubic feet per minute), and the plans can be scaled upwards for larger air flows. It is claimed to be 50 to 70 percent efficient. Write: U-Learn, University of Saskatchewan Extension Division, Saskatoon, Saskatchewan, Canada, S7N 0W0, and ask for the engineering bulletin entitled *An Air-To-Air Heat Exchanger for Residences.*

Lossnay

Manufactured by Mitsubishi of Japan, the Lossnay heat exchanger features a waterpermeable heat transfer surface that is especially useful in humid climates. Because the Lossnay unit is capable of removing moisture from incoming air before it reaches the house, it claims to be two to three times more effective in reducing summer energy costs than units that do not remove moisture from the air. Unfortunately, there is a trade-off. Wa-

The Heart of a Heat Exchanger

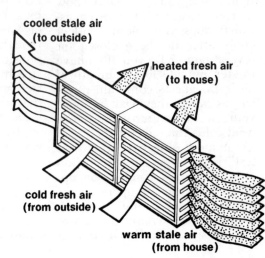

cooled stale air (to outside)

heated fresh air (to house)

cold fresh air (from outside)

warm stale air (from house)

In an air-to-air heat exchanger, two air streams are made to flow past each other, separated by a metal, plastic or specially treated paper barrier. Although the two air streams never physically mix, heat from the warmer stream passes through the barrier into the cooler stream. The illustration shows how a heat exchanger works in winter, when an exhaust stream of warm stale air is used to preheat an incoming stream of cold fresh air.

terborne contaminants can also pass through the permeable barrier, so the Lossnay might not be quite as effective in removing indoor pollution. The basic unit costs about $200, carries an impressive ten-year guarantee, and is capable of ventilating up to 1,200 square feet of floor plan. It is claimed to be 75 percent efficient. Write: Mike Thomas, Melco Environmental Products, 3030 E. Victoria St., Compton, California 90221.

Van Ee

Dick Van Ee of the University of Saskatchewan offers a prefab version of the do-it-yourself design mentioned earlier. A stripped version (requiring owner-installed ducts and blowers) costs $200 postpaid; a ready-to-mount unit costs $375 postpaid. Write: Dick Van Ee, RR #3 Saskatoon, Saskatchewan, Canada S7K 3J6.

Enercon

Operating at an impressive 85 percent efficiency with flow rates as high as 400 cfm, the Enercon heat exchanger is well suited for larger buildings. The unit comes complete, except for the external duct work, and costs $995. Write: Dennis Rogoza, Enercon Industries, 2073 Cornwall St., Regina, Saskatchewan, Canada S4P 2K6.

The problem of figuring costs is one that's plagued Gene from the start because of the unusual way his home's components interlock with and influence one another. "The thing to remember is that my house is an entire system in itself," he said, "and not just a collection of unrelated subsystems."

An example of this interlocking design is Gene's back-up baseboard heating system. The extra insulation in the walls raised the home's initial costs, but allowed the amount of baseboard radiators to be reduced from a standard 120 feet to just 46 feet—a substantial savings. "And even 46 feet turned out to be more than I needed," Gene said.

The savings continued to snowball: It would have been wasteful to install a full-sized boiler to power just 46 feet of baseboard, so Gene designed his plumbing such that the baseboard radiators simply steal whatever heat is needed from the home's hot-tap water supply. This greatly simplified the plumbing and completely eliminated the need for a separate space-heating furnace or boiler. The savings of *not* having to buy and install a boiler were large enough to offset most of the extra costs of the insulation which had made these savings possible in the first place.

To save energy in his dual-purpose water heating system, Gene used a "Paloma-Pak Boiler"; a tiny 46-pound, vacuum-cleaner-sized device hung on the cellar wall. Because it's so small, the natural gas-fueled boiler has very little mass of its own; in fact, it holds only about two pounds of water at any given time. There's so little mass, the

Paloma-Pak reaches full operating temperature almost instantly and puts out a steady stream of hot water with very high efficiency. Heated water is stored between firings in a nearby heavily insulated water tank which has no heating element of its own. (This tank supplies hot water directly to the baseboard radiators and simultaneously provides hot water to the home's taps through a heat exchanger.)

Gene used similar inventiveness in designing the home's electrical systems. Rather than using in-the-wall switches and outlets, he installed a type of surface wiring called "flat conductor cable" manufactured by ITE Gould. These strips of three-conductor wire run above the baseboard radiators on the inside surfaces of the home's walls. Switches and outlets can be snapped in place as needed anywhere along the cable. Because no holes for wiring or electrical boxes are cut in the exterior walls, the walls' thermal barrier remains intact. "Using flat cable saved money, too," said Gene, "both in labor, because cable just staples in place, and in wiring costs. Flat cable costs about 65 cents per foot, but I estimate I

The double walls were made of 2 x 4 studs on 24-inch centers, and were raised into place in the conventional manner. Because the final wall thickness is determined by the positioning of the inner-wall section, double-wall homes are extremely simple to custom-tailor to an unusually cold or windy site.

saved about 250 feet of branch wiring in the walls."

As the house was being built, Gene also saw a way to reduce construction costs even further and to avoid potential problems with workmen. "Let-in corner bracing (where studs are chiseled out to accept a diagonal corner brace) is labor intensive and difficult to do accurately," he said. "There's a product called Thermo-Ply that is designed to be nailed directly to the outer surface of studs. It's only an eighth of an inch thick, so it doesn't get in the way, but it's immensely strong and allows you to eliminate diagonal corner bracing completely. It's faster, cheaper, and in many cases, stronger." Gene now suggests that two sheets of Thermo-Ply butted end to end be used at each corner of the framing, in place of standard corner braces.

I asked Gene to summarize what made his design different from the other double-wall homes being built around the country. "First of all," he said, "the airlock vestibules are external, instead of being enclosed within a heated space. I feel this is more effective. Second, my ceilings are seven feet three inches high, which is anywhere from three to nine inches shorter than normal. The loss of headroom doesn't matter to anyone of average height, and it reduces the space that must be heated. Third, the outside insulated wall runs from the foundation to the roofline, instead of from the floor up. Fourth, I used box beams

(which can be stuffed with insulation) over doors and windows instead of using solid wooden (and low R) headers. I also sheathed the entire house in polystyrene tongue-and-groove boards to improve the insulation and reduce air infiltration and intrusion. Fifth, I paid special attention to air-tightness. The vapor barrier is six-mil polyethylene, and I used large overlaps at the ceiling and floors to create a continuous barrier, completely enclosing the heated area. Finally, wherever we had to pierce the barrier—for doors and windows, for example—I filled the opening in the frame with an expanding foam product to make sure there would be no air leaks at all. In fact, when the house is closed up, the only opening is the bathroom roof vent, and that's protected from heat loss by an internal valve."

All these techniques add up to impressive performance at reasonable cost. "Yes, the extra insulation costs more at the outset," Gene admits, "but the thermal performance of the walls allows me to save elsewhere. The lack of a separate furnace, for example, and the simplified plumbing and electrical work, offset most of the extra costs right off the bat." In fact, Gene claims that the materials for his prototype house cost just $30,000; no more than a standardly constructed home with the same floor plan. His figures may be a little low, because many products used in the house were donated free by manufacturers and distributors. Nevertheless, a rule of thumb for houses of this type states that they should cost just five to seven percent more than utterly conventional homes; an amount the minuscule fuel bills almost immediately recoup.

And "minuscule" is no exaggeration. According to John Gallant, who purchased the house from Gene last winter, total annual energy bills for everything—lights, appliances, hot water, and heating—amount to about $200, with only $50 of that directly attributable to space heating. For comparison, John told me his former residence cost about $600 per year for fuel, although it was no larger than the house Gene built. "Although the costs are higher than Gene first estimated," John said, "I'm still satisfied." And John's not the easiest man to please. He made his decision to purchase Gene's house as a homeowner first and as a conservation enthusiast second.

"It's true the house wasn't perfect," Gene said. "After all, it

was a prototype." Some of the problems that did occur were inadvertently masked by Gene's own enthusiasm during the time he lived in the house. As he told me, "A problem is only a problem if someone defines it that way." Because of this philosophy, some early statements of the home's performance published by Gene and others may not accurately reflect real-life conditions. For example, John Gallant could not duplicate Gene's extremely low fuel use, even though the Gallant's bills were still small. Overheating and glare were also troublesome, due to the home's too-large south windows. Peg Leger, Gene's wife, occasionally had to wear sunglasses indoors. Better screening, awnings or reflective films could help solve this.

When I visited Gene's house, I saw a potentially serious flaw in the extreme tightness that could lead to stuffiness, odors and excessive humidity. Gene coped with the extreme tightness by opening the windows all day during the summer and for up to five

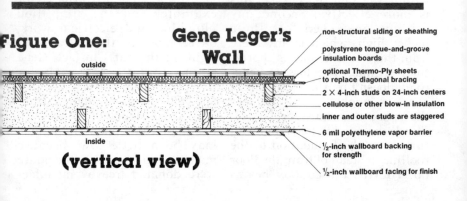

Figure One: Gene Leger's Wall

outside

inside

(vertical view)

non-structural siding or sheathing

polystyrene tongue-and-groove insulation boards

optional Thermo-Ply sheets to replace diagonal bracing

2 × 4-inch studs on 24-inch centers

cellulose or other blow-in insulation

inner and outer studs are staggered

6 mil polyethylene vapor barrier

1/2-inch wallboard backing for strength

1/2-inch wallboard facing for finish

hours a day in winter. Although Gene claimed this had no effect on the home's temperatures or fuel use, opening a window cannot be considered an effective conservation strategy, and in fact, defeats the purpose of building an airtight house in the first place.

My suspicions were confirmed by the Gallants after they moved in. "I'd wake up in the morning, and couldn't see out the windows because of the condensation," John told me. "If it was really cold, there'd be puddles on the window sills with water running down the walls. I was worried about the walls rotting."

For more information:
Gene Leger
Vista Homes
Box 95
E. Pepperell, MA 01437

Paloma-Pak Boilers
NEGEA Energy Products Inc.
60 Quinsigamond Ave.
Worcester, MA 01613

Thermo-Ply
Simplex Products Group
3000 W. Beecher Road
Box 10
Adrian, MI 49221

To correct things, Gene installed an air-to-air heat exchanger to help ventilate and dehumidify the house. "It's helping," John reports. "Humidity is averaging about 60 percent now, and condensation is less of a problem." Most people feel comfortable with humidity levels between 30 and 50 percent. If 60 percent turns out to be unacceptably high, Gene can either install a small, low-wattage fan to help circulate dehumidified air throughout the house or install a second heat exchanger.

Problems like these should not overshadow the valid concepts that Gene is trying to prove. Thick, airtight double walls, innovative plumbing, heating, electrical and ventilation systems, and striving towards low-cost quality construction techniques are all sound ideas— but as with any new technique, there are bugs to be worked out. Only by building new homes, and learning from them, can we bring new concepts in efficient housing off the drawing boards and into America's neighborhoods.

"It's not a question if the design works," Gene said. "It's just a question of how well it works. We've got to look at the future and get new ideas out to the public. The only way we're going to solve our energy problems is by giving every homeowner a chance to do his part without going broke."

GUIDELINES FOR GOING UNDERGROUND

*Building an underground home involves
more than just renting a backhoe.
Careful pre-evaluation and planning
can prevent some costly,
and aggravating, mistakes.*

The attractions of earth-sheltered architecture include land conservation, long-lasting structures and reduced fuel use. But the biggest news usually seems to be that those advantages are possible in bright, sunny buildings with views out across the landscape.

How is this possible? It's because underground buildings have earth-covered roofs and have protecting earth at most outside walls, but they need not be deep below grade. We can build underground in any of the ways shown in these cross sections. A number of do's, don'ts, new opportunities and possible mistakes stand out when we plan to go underground. Here are some of the most common ones.

Site Conditions

It's essential to build above the water table. That means determining the highest (not average) level that groundwater may reach at the building site. Sources for that information are test borings by a soils engineer, the Soil Conservation Service and sometimes observant neighbors. Land with high water tables is often ideal for building on grade, then berming earth around the sides and over the top of the structure.

Codes

Building codes need not pose problems for well-designed underground buildings. The Uniform Building Code requires operable windows (or outside doors) in bedrooms. The reason is fire exits. That's fine. We wouldn't want these rooms without safe ways out. Natural light is required throughout most rooms of a house. Since underground houses can easily be designed to look out to open vistas, courtyards and light wells, that's fine too.

Design

Good underground design is based on the local climate and the specific character of the site. A plan designed for one site can never blindly be built on another site. All sorts of embarrassments can happen when that's attempted: slopes go the wrong way, trees pop up in unexpected places, and all of the previous careful planning for the wise use of sun and breezes goes haywire.

Gently and inconspicuously tucking the building into the site can provide beautiful results. An underground building can achieve a wonderful repose on the land. Beware of jarring retaining walls, overbearing garage doors and other features that would mar that sense of repose. Really good underground buildings present themselves to us in a very graceful manner.

Design takes time. Many people, charged up with the excitement of going underground, want to start digging right away! That enthusiasm is great, but the crucial design decisions that will shape the face of the land for many lifetimes and affect thousands of dollars must go through a lot of churning and hard re-evaluation.

To simplify is crucial. This is sometimes a bitter lesson. The temptation to go overboard is very common on a first underground project. It is often puzzling to see the complicated roofs, the maze-like floor plans full of wasted space and extensive gadgetry proposed for many first projects. The more we discipline ourselves toward simple,

compact and well-thought-out buildings, the better the results will be.

A real delight about going underground is that the building changes for the better as the years go by. Wildlife makes itself at home. Vines grow. The succession of native plants keeps us alert to the seasons. Don't worry if on move-in day the building looks somehow unfinished. It is unfinished. But the rest of the work will now be done by nature.

Heat Leaks

Often when we think about the energy efficiency of underground buildings we conjure up images of a stable 55° F environment that needs hardly any fuel.

However, when we get to designing a building in which we want to live or work, the picture changes. We might put in windows and skylights facing directions other than south for light and view. We put in doors. We put in vent pipes and flues. Suddenly we find that the design is poked thoroughly full of holes. Also, the earth cover on the roof is quite shallow now in an effort to trim structural costs. No constant 55° F up there! And somehow the structure begins to bristle with heat bleeding projections. The building now has heat leaks galore. Even with proper passive solar orientation, those heat leaks can be significant problems. Here are some ways we cut down all the unanticipated loss.

Avoid cantilever roof slabs and parapet walls. They are very tempting to use. The designers of the (current) first generation of underground buildings learned the lesson well: those projections are a significant source of heat loss.

Avoid retaining walls that are extensions of the building's structure. These bleed heat, too.

Evaluate the use of skylights very carefully. Conventional skylights are notorious for their potential water leaks and have a way of letting heat pour out in the winter and in, in the summer. A better approach is roof monitors with south-facing glazing to replace the usual plastic dome.

Insulate well around the entire building. Earth will not do the job by itself. Earth is great at moderating temperature around a building and protecting it from scouring winds, but insulation should be used .

Materials

It's a pleasure to work with materials for underground construction: they're so substantial. They have to be. Everybody hates the thought of all that digging to make repairs.

Superior underground waterproofings are much more costly than shingles, but they sure last longer. It's important to use only waterproofing products which the manufacturer specifically recommends, in literature, for underground use. Most any waterproofing application must be treated as a "system" using the primers, edge treatments and accessories as recommended by the

Solaria, a design by architect Malcolm Wells, is shown here in 1974 just before the Butyl rubber sheet was laid on the roof. An earth-covered house heated by a Thomason "Solaris" solar system; it used almost no fuel during its first all-winter test.

Solaria, two years later, with the rooftop land-scape grown firmly in place.

David Deppen is an architect in Portland, Oregon, who specializes in ecologically sound architecture.

103

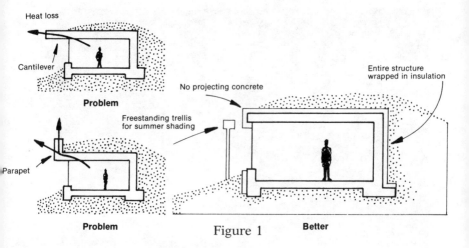

Figure 1

manufacturer. There are many rubberized liquid and Butyl sheet waterproofings available. The best way to get them is usually through a local commercial waterproofing contractor. You want something better than the usual waterproofing that's applied to the outside of basement walls. But whatever material you use, the crucial factor is the quality of workmanship during installation. A careful do-it-yourself job might even be better than a contractor's work.

Rigid insulation boards all around the structure and in contact with earth must be selected with one overriding concern: they must be of a type which will not eventually soak up water. Wet insulation is worthless. Check manufacturer's literature to be sure a product is recommended for soil contact and use in water-logged conditions. Extruded polystyrene, also known as blue Styrofoam, is often the best choice in all areas of the United States outside of the very

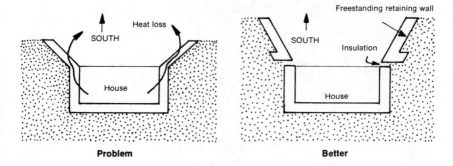

Figure 2

Figure 3

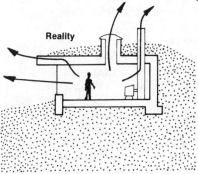

dry soil of the Southwest.

Humidity

Humidity levels need be no special problem in a properly designed building if we remember a few basics. In a new building, curing concrete releases moisture into the interior air. This means a dehumidifier is usually necessary for perhaps the first two years as the structure dries out. Remember that most conventional buildings are annoyingly dry in the winter heating season. Our goal must be to produce the most healthful humidity level.

Landscaping

A reasonable depth of earth cover on a roof often ranges from 1½ to 2 feet. At less than 1½ feet the soil is prone to dry out too quickly in the summer. Over 2 feet the structural support costs become quite high.

Grading all slopes away from the building is a must. There should be gentle slopes on rooftop areas to prevent ponding. General site slopes toward the

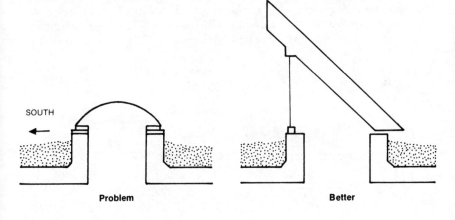

Figure 4

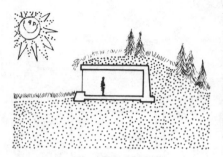

building must be diverted before they reach the building, usually by gentle drainage channels. Otherwise the building may be subjected to undue water pressure.

Deep mulching on top of the soil provides a lightweight covering that helps retain soil moisture, prevents erosion and provides a protective cover for the host of young plants establishing themselves on the roof and berms. Ideal mulches in this case are those that blend with the landscape and decompose rather quickly. No bark chunks!

Rooftop plantings may include some transplanted native shrubs and ground covers with the major portion of the roof allowed to go through natural suc-

cession that determines what's best suited for that place. Yes, it takes a bit of courage to let that happen, but the watering, inevitable replacing and tending to exotics which don't belong there isn't really very sensible. Our spirits soar when the first wild flowers appear. They're hardy, cheery and colorful. It's hard to imagine better rooftop citizens.

Before Digging In

Question: *Have you ever seen earth-sheltered houses collapse?*
Malcolm Wells, architect: *No, but then I've had my fingers crossed for years.*

When it comes to earth-sheltered housing, there's no such thing as luck. At some point a structural engineer must review your plans. It will prevent catastrophe and could even save you a bundle on construction costs.

The first step in going underground is to learn more about the subject. Two good sources of information are the Clearing House of Earth-Covered Buildings, School of Architecture, University of Texas at Arlington, Arlington, TX 76019; and The

Figure 5

Underground Space Center, 112 Civil and Mineral Engineering Department, University of Minnesota, Minneapolis, MN 55455. Three good books on construction and design are: *Earth-Sheltered Housing Designs*, Van Nostrand Reinhold Co., 135 West 50th St., New York, NY 10020 ($9.95); *Underground Designs*, Malcolm Wells, Box 1149, Brewster, MA 02631 ($6.00); *Earth Integrated Architecture*, College of Architecture, Arizona State University, Tempe, AZ 85281 ($10.00).

After studying a variety of house designs, you'll have a better idea of what you want. Then you can draw up a set of plans yourself, consult with an architect, or buy a set (for $100 to $300) from one of several firms that market underground designs.

Those mail-order plans are working drawings signed by a professional architect or engineer who takes responsibility for their structural soundness. Because those plans are sent every-where in the nation, the house is designed for the worst possible soil conditions. But the soil on your site may be considerably lighter and firmer, so you don't need as much strength in your roof and footings.

What to do? Take your plans to a local engineer. You may spend up to several hundred dollars on his services and soil borings, but the results may save you several thousand dollars in the construction phase.

If you work with an architect, he will consult with a local structural engineer. If you draw up your own plans and take them directly to a building contractor, the building contractor undoubtedly will have them approved by a structural engineer. So there's no escape, and thankfully so. If your plans aren't feasible, the engineer will rip them to shreds. The lesson is: unless you have a knowledge of materials and stress limits, it's best to work with a local engineer from the start.

OLD HOUSE, NEW WATER WALL

"I like water as a thermal mass because it's cheap and extremely flexible."

Jude Noland and husband Tim Magee relax in the solar-heated warmth of their living room. By painting the thermal storage tubes midnight-blue, by varying their heights, and by using plants, Tim made his water wall an attractive focal point for the home's main floor.

Tim Magee likes a simple natural approach to building. And in his home town of Seattle—one of America's cloudiest, rainiest port cities, where nothing is more natural than water—Magee has put water and sunshine to work. Built a wall of water, in fact, to store solar heat. It's an innovation that has helped him cut his home heating bill by a phenomenal 94 percent, from $1,100 to just $70 a year.

Magee's living room water wall consists of 20 midnight-blue metal cylinders of various diameters and heights, rubbercoated on the inside, filled with ordinary tap water, decorated with house plants and artwork, and placed next to 225 square feet of south-facing windows.

Now, Seattle is not what you'd call an ideal solar climate. In the city, the sun shines less than half the time year-round, less than three days in ten in the winter. Still, Magee's windows and water tubes work well, catching what little sun there is and making his 70-year-old, 1,400-square-foot, two-

Water Wall Retrofit

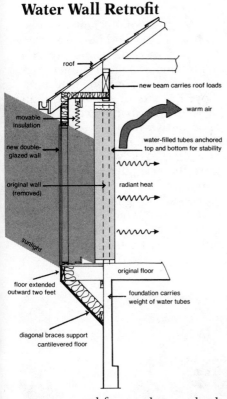

roof →

→ new beam carries roof loads

warm air

movable insulation

water-filled tubes anchored top and bottom for stability

new double-glazed wall

original wall (removed)

radiant heat

sunlight

original floor

floor extended outward two feet

foundation carries weight of water tubes

diagonal braces support cantilevered floor

story, wood-frame house both more comfortable and more efficient. Other things help, too: The solar windows and water tubes were added to the house as part of an extensive, $10,000 retrofit that included thermal window curtains, extra insulation totaling R-19 in the walls and R-38 in the attic, and replacement of a forced-air oil furnace with an airtight wood stove. "Conservation was the key," Magee says, "but the solar heat stored in the water wall was the clincher."

Magee, 29, is a trained botanist who's been working in greenhouses since he was 10 years old. He's also a self-taught solar pioneer who built Seattle's first solar greenhouse. "Water was what I started with in building the greenhouses," Magee says. "I used barrels I found for free at boat yards and construction sites. I'd just keep my eyes open and I'd find them."

In his sun-warmed, sun-lighted living room where the blue water tubes sit like avant-garde sculpture, two, three, six, and eight feet tall, Magee explains that he never seriously considered using any mass other than water when he decided to retrofit his house in 1979. "I like water because it's cheap and extremely flexible," he says. "Take it away. Put it back. Move it. Get tired of barrels or tubes, move them. A quick remodel."

Magee believes that water is the obvious thermal mass for most residential retrofitting, not just in soggy Seattle. But in places like Seattle, he stresses, water is especially useful because it heats up quickly in those rare winter minutes when the clouds part. "Water absorbs and transfers heat quickly," he says, "almost like breathing with the changes in weather."

Though sold on the advantages of water as thermal mass, Magee isn't as pleased with the metal tubes he used. He'd prefer to use fiber glass tubes now, the kind available from Solar Components Corporation (Kalwall) or from various manufacturers of fiber glass miscellany.

Magee's tubes were originally designed for high-pressure air ducting and are rubber-coated on the inside. While they cost slightly less than fiber glass tubes (which average $10–$11 a foot or around $85 for an eight-footer), they leaked occasionally and their components were hard to find.

"The other problem we ran into," he says, "is that in the early stages of solar design, no one knew how much storage mass you needed. No one had *any* idea. So we just added and took away until we found an amount that seemed to be right. What we ended up with is one of the simplest, cheapest, passive solar designs that works well in a rainy, cloudy climate."

Magee explains how the tube wall was built and how it works: Much the way he would proceed in building a series of sliding glass doors or bay windows, Magee removed the entire south wall in the living room and extended the floor outward by two feet. (See diagram.) Ten new windows, 34 x 76 inches each, were installed to form the new outside wall. These windows were manufacturing "seconds"—slightly flawed, tempered glass intended for use as patio doors, and costing $25 a pair. Added to that were two op-

*Tim Magee's water wall retrofit helped to reduce his heating bills from a major expense to a petty-cash item. Note the cantilevering of the double-glazed south wall: This enabled Tim to place the solar-heated water tubes (visible through the glass) directly over the foundation wall, where the tubes' extra weight is no problem.—**Inset**—Before the retrofit, the 70-year-old home's south wall was bland. Worse, a combination of small windows and wide eaves meant that solar gain was nil.*

erable windows, flooring to match the original, gypsum board, and trim, along with the 20 storage tubes, an insulating night-curtain and some fresh-air vents to prevent summertime overheating.

"For this much glass in this climate, Magee says, "the complement of water should be around six gallons per square foot of south-facing glass. We didn't want to have a bunch of boring tubes, so we cut different sizes, and we just kept adding them all up and shoving them in there until we had the six gallons per square foot, or around three-quarters of a cubic foot of water per square foot of glass."

The tubes are 12, 14, 16, and 18 inches in diameter. Of these, the 12-inch size seems the most suitable in this type of home, maintaining a 65-degree minimum on even the worst days and warming to a toasty 85 degrees on sunny days. "On a January evening, you can sit next to these tubes in your shirt-sleeves and be quite cozy," Magee says. The larger-diameter tubes don't get nearly as warm.

The tubes are placed just inside the new windows and therefore right over the foundation, and are bracketed to the floor so they can't be knocked over. The largest tubes each weigh 300 pounds; together, all the tubes weigh less than the original wall and less than a roomful of people, Magee says. The tubes are filled with plain water. "What I did was take a little motor oil and drip it on top of the water in the sealed container," he says. (The thin, float-ing film of oil prevents evaporation of the water.) "Nothing is going to grow in water that light can't get to. If you were using transparent tubes, you might want to put chlorine bleach in them."

As a feature of the house, the tubes certainly are distinctive, yet they do fit the decor. "Many people never realize that these tubes have anything to do with solar heating. The baby sitter once took a call from some guy asking where we got the tubes and she stood looking at them and said: 'Tubes, what tubes?' "

Still to be added to the solar system is a movable canvas awning to shade the window in summer. When the floor was extended outward, the shading from the original 30-inch eave on the house was lost. The manually operated fresh-air vents below the window wall were installed to compensate for the eave, but by themselves, weren't enough to prevent overheating. "If I were building the wall again," Tim says, "I'd skip the vents altogether and just use shading. It's simpler."

How well does the solar system work?

To monitor it closely this past winter, Magee temporarily installed five thermostatically controlled electric heaters as a solar back-up and simply did not use his wood stove because its consumption is hard to measure. He hung up five maximum/minimum thermometers and connected a kilowatt-hour meter to the heaters. Thus, he could measure inside/outside temperature, temperature of the thermal mass water, and daily kilowatt-hour usage. During the winter, the house was kept between 55 and 68 degrees F. On the coldest, cloudiest, December day, the house used 35 kilowatt-hours; on the sunny days, the heaters didn't come on at all. And for the entire last winter—November to May—the Magee house used 4,000 kilowatt-hours (at 1.75 cents a kilowatt-hour) of electricity. Cost: $70.

Magee has no doubt that masonry and rock can be aesthetically pleasing. And he's especially fond of the idea of using adobe for thermal mass in desert climates. But, where cost and flexibility are the issues, water wins in his mind.

"Look," he says, "when you get down to the point at which your heating bill is under $100 a year because of conservation work you've done or a solar application, how much money can you justify putting into mass?" It just doesn't make sense, he figures, to get carried away—especially in a mild climate.

"A lot of people have this idea that they are going to do a— WOW!—solar house, and they get all this glass and this mass and they spend thousands and thousands of dollars on exotic computer-controlled rock bin systems and so on. But, with a truly simple approach, using a conventional and passive solar heating system, how can you justify that cost? As far as I can see, water is the simplest and best answer."

Well, perhaps with one exception: Low mass. Maybe even no mass, or at least, none beyond the house itself. "I think the house of the future may be a highly insulated, low-mass building," he says. "Even in retrofits. The more you insulate your house, the less solar gain you need. Window area gets progressively smaller and smaller.

"Consequently, the less window area you have, the less mass you are going to need to complement it. Pretty soon, when you get down to a small enough window area, just your house itself is going to have mass in it enough— plaster walls and so on. You don't need to add anything, not even water."

Along this line, Rainshadow, Magee's Seattle-based solar company, recently made a conservation-solar retrofit, building water mass into the design. But the mass was left out of the house, as an experiment. The house features an attached greenhouse and conventional gas furnace. So far, through one winter—admittedly, a mild one even for Seattle—the occupants say the house was comfortable, and they were satisfied with the low gas bills.

"Dollar for dollar in energy savings, conservation is the best thing for you," Magee insists. "Added mass comes second. But if you *do* add mass," he says with a smile, "I don't think you can do better than water."

GLOSSARY

Absorber plate—The surface of a collector, generally faced with a matte black-metallic material, which absorbs solar radiation and converts it to heat energy.

Activated charcoal—(also called "active carbon.") A highly absorbent form of charcoal obtained by heating charcoal granules to drive out trapped gases. Activated charcoal is frequently used to filter, deodorize and cleanse gases and some liquids.

Active solar—Any solar energy system that uses external mechanical power to move heat from where it's collected to someplace else for use or storage. Solar energy systems are either active, passive or hybrid (a combination of the two). Passive, unlike active, operates under its own power and uses or stores heat where it's collected.

Air change—The exchange of one volume of air for another. If a solar collector has one air change per minute, it means that the collector's entire volume of air is replaced every 60 seconds.

Air gap—A narrow air-filled space. If the air within the gap moves, the gap functions as a narrow duct. If the air within the gap is stagnant, then the gap functions as an insulating layer.

Airlock entry—Two doors separated by a short vestibule or hall. Because only one door is used at a time, the home's interior is never directly opened to the outside.

Airway—A passage or duct through which air flows. In solar collectors, *airways* are often created by inserting *baffles* within an *air gap*.

Baffles—Solid obstructions used to regulate the passage or alter the direction of flow of a gas or liquid.

Batten—A narrow strip of wood covering a vertical joint or seam. Useful in keeping out water ("batten the hatches!") as well as being decorative. "Board and batten" is a style of house siding that consists of foot-wide vertical planks and two-inch-wide battens covering their joints.

Berm—An earthen bank built against the roof or exterior of a house. A bermed house (also known as semi-recessed) is one whose construction is above ground but has earth banked over its roof and against its north, east and west sides to create semi-underground effect.

Brace—An inclined or angled board that stiffens a wall, floor or roof. Corner braces are used at the ends of walls to resist side-to-side "racking" forces. The most common form of corner brace is a let-in 2 x 4 running diagonally across the outside of a stud wall.

Btu—The amount of energy needed to raise one pound (one pint) of water 1° F. The burning of a single match gives off approximately one Btu of heat. A gallon of oil burned in the average home's furnace produces

113

about 100,000 Btus of heat.

Comfort zone—(1) The portions of a room (usually from the floor to head-height) in which temperatures and humidity must be controlled. (2) The range of temperatures and humidity in which 50 percent of all adults are comfortable.

Conduction—The transmission of something (electricity, heat, light, sound, etc.) through a medium or passage. A good conductor is a substance that permits the material being conducted to flow from one point to another without reducing the material's characteristics. Insulation is a poor conductor of heat; metal, which permits heat to pass through it, is a good conductor.

Convective loop—The circular movement of heat within a closed fluid system in accordance with the natural principle that warm air (or any fluid) rises, cool air falls.

Crosscut—In carpentry, a cut made across the grain of a board, or the saw used to make such a cut.

Dado—A rectangular groove cut in the surface of a board, or the act of cutting such a groove. When a second board or framing member is inserted into a dado, the resulting assembly is called a "dado joint."

Deburr—To smooth a piece of metal of sharp edges caused by machining.

Degree day—An indication of heating needs based on the difference between the average daily temperature and an assumed steady indoor temperature of 65° F. A 24-hour period with an average temperature of 60° F rates five degree days; a daily average of 0° F rates 65 degree days. Degree days can be totaled to obtain seasonal or yearly heating needs.

Down spout—An enclosed pipe which carries water from an elevated location to a lower one. Rain gutters along a roof's edge are usually equipped with down spouts to carry runoff to the ground or to a cistern.

Drumwall—A heat-storing system consisting of water-filled metal oil drums which are painted flat black and stacked one atop the other to form a "wall." Used in passive solar homes and greenhouses to absorb daytime heat received through south-facing glass and to radiate it into the room at night.

Fascia—The flat, horizontal member of a structure; generally between moldings or sections.

Glazing—A covering of transparent or translucent material (glass or plastic) used for admitting light.

Gutter—Sometimes called an "edge trough" or "eave trough." A shallow U-shaped channel set below the edges of a roof to collect and carry off rainwater.

Insolation—The total amount of solar energy—direct, diffuse and reflected—striking a surface exposed to the sky. *Not* a misspelling of "insulation."

Joist—One of a series of horizontal parallel pieces of lumber that comprise the skeleton of a floor or ceiling.

Lath—A lightweight strip or

mesh of wood or metal used as a supporting structure for plaster, stucco, slate, tiles, etc.

Ledger strip—A strip of lumber, nailed to a larger framing member or foundation, that is used to support the ends of joists.

Let-in—"Let-in" means to set flush with the surface of the surrounding structure. For example, braces are often let-in by chiseling or cutting away the wall's studs.

Load-bearing wall—Some people call it a bearing wall. It carries a load in addition to its own weight.

O.C.—Stands for "on center." It measures the spacing of wall studs, rafters, joists, etc., from the exact center of one framing member to the exact center of the next. Most residential exterior walls, for example, have 2 x 4 studs 16" o.c.

Ozone—A variant form of oxygen composed of three molecules instead of the normal two. Ozone is created naturally by lightning and sunlight, and can be manufactured from ordinary oxygen with high voltage sparks or ultraviolet radiation. Ozone can be used as a deodorant or a sterilizing agent.

Payback period—The time it takes for an energy modification to pay for itself through savings on fuel. For example, if you install $400 worth of attic insulation and as a result save $200 a year on your oil bill, the payback period is two years.

Plate—The horizontal (and usually topmost) member of a structure which tops off or caps a frame.

R-factor—This is a measurement of a material's tendency to retard the flow of heat through it. The higher the R-factor, the greater the material's insulating value.

Rabbet—A groove cut along the corner edge of a board.

Racking—What happens to a rectangular structure when it gets pushed on one side? It wants to sway. Racking is prevented by braces within the rectangle.

Retrofit—The modification of an existing home with new equipment in order to make it more energy-efficient. Derived from the term "retroactive refitting."

Rip—In carpentry, a cut made with the grain of a board or the saw used to make such a cut.

Roof washer—A device using a flow or spray of water to cleanse a roof of loose debris and dirt. Used in conjunction with cisterns, roof washers minimize the job of filtering and purifying collected rainwater.

Sill—The horizontal (and usually bottommost) member of a structure that supports an upright frame. Also called the "sole" or the "base."

Soffit—The underside of a structural member of a building: beam, arch, etc.

Solar collector—Any of a wide variety of devices (from ordinary windows to Trombe walls) that collect solar energy and convert it to heat.

Space conditioning—The heating, cooling, humidifying or dehumidifying of air in the space enclosed by a home's four walls. It has nothing to do with the training of astronauts.

Stud—One of a series of vertical pieces of lumber that comprises the skeleton of a wall.

Thermal chimney—A nonmechanical means of providing air movement, consisting of a duct or passage in which warm air can rise to create natural convective ventilation.

Thermal mass—The amount of potential heat storage capacity of a material or system. The heavier a material, the more heat it can store. Adobe walls, 55-gallon drums of water and bins of rock are common examples.

Trombe wall—Named after its French inventor, Felix Trombe, it is a passive solar device consisting of a masonry wall that heats up because it's covered on one side (the one facing the sun), by glazing about 6 inches away from the wall.

Ultraviolet radiation—An intense form of electromagnetic radiation falling between the violet portion of the visible spectrum, and X rays. Ultraviolet radiation is a normal component of sunlight (it's what causes sunburn) and can be produced artificially with mercury-vapor lamps. When intensely concentrated, it can be used to sterilize gases, liquids and solid surfaces.